D1823835

9788513119464

A STUD FARM DIARY

By HUMPHREY S. FINNEY

J. A. Allen & Co Ltd
1973

85131 194 6

Published by J. A. Allen & Co Ltd
1 Lower Grosvenor Place
London

Printed in Great Britain by
Lewis Reprints Ltd.
member of Brown Knight & Truscott Group
London and Tonbridge

INTRODUCTION

More than forty years ago, it was the writer's pleasure to have served for better than a decade as Stud Manager for the Labrot family in Maryland. There the Holly Beach Farm spread over more than 2500 acres along the shores of the Chesapeake Bay. It was a happy association, one whose wide range of responsibilities afforded a young man with a taste for journalism ample material for contributions to the then new breeding magazine, *The Blood-Horse*.

For more than a year this magazine published weekly a diary, wherein were recounted the day-by-day activities of the manager of the Labrot stud farm, his family and his loyal corps of assistants. For obvious reasons a nom-de-plume (Nothing Venture) was used. The location of the farm, its name and those of the horses thereon were likewise disguised.

The Stud Farm Diary was published in limited edition by *The Blood-Horse* in December 1936. It was soon out of print and the book was unavailable until Stacy Lloyd, then publisher of *The Chronicle*, undertook its reproduction in 1949. This reprinting has also long been unavailable.

The author has come to the conclusion that another edition is about due. This project is being undertaken by the American Racing Publications, Inc., of Middleburg, Virginia, who will distribute the current edition of the Diary. Nothing has been added to, or changed in the original material. Other than the advances made in veterinary medicine during the past quarter century (penicillin, antibiotics, etc., were unheard of in those days), there is little difference in practical stud management today from what made sense in 1935.

HUMPHREY S. FINNEY

Versailles, Kentucky
1973

FOREWORD — 1949

When Humphrey S. Finney was gaining the experience in the field that makes his advice on all matters pertaining to the Thoroughbred sought from one end of the country to the other, he was managing the stud at Holly Beach Farm, Annapolis, Md., and writing a diary. As this stud was then one of the larger establishments in the country, a cycle of a year brought the whole gamut of a Thoroughbred breeder's experiences before the astute eye of Mr. Finney.

This diary, first published by THE BLOOD-HORSE *in 1935, is a handbook of practical experience from foaling to training, that only one with Mr. Finney's great knowledge could write. He is able to sift the good and the bad and to add from his own store of knowledge a wealth of practices accumulated in England as well as in this country. This little handbook is one for horsemen young and old, for the information it contains is the actual experiences of men steeped in the world of Thoroughbred breeding and compiled by a master horseman in book form. As Mr. Estes of* THE BLOOD-HORSE *wrote in his foreword to Mr. Finney's Diary, "It is a unique and valuable contribution to the literature of the turf."*

STACY B. LLOYD,
Publisher, The Chronicle

A STUD FARM DIARY

IN a second-hand bookshop in London a few years ago I picked up a book by a favorite author, Sir H. Rider Haggard, entitled *A Farmer's Year*, for a few pence. I discovered it to be a more or less complete record of the author's farming activities on his Norfolk estates for a whole year, written as events transpired and in the form of a diary containing his reactions to the various phases of farming. It occurred to me, on running across this old book a few days ago, that readers of THE BLOOD-HORSE who are not familiar with operations on a large stud farm might be interested in something of a similar nature describing, as they take place throughout the year, the different operations which make up the studmaster's calendar, without, however, attempting to prescribe the procedure which any other farm should follow.

The stud whereof this is written is a large one, with close to 50 mares. It has a couple of home sires and patronizes some of the better ones away. In times past it has turned out its share of winners. I propose to call this farm, for want of a better name, Sleepy Hollow Stud, and if there be a farm of that name anywhere, I crave its indulgence. At the farm now there are thirty-odd weanlings, a score of yearlings which are in training, though no attempt has yet been made to try them. The personnel of the farm is divided between white foremen and colored grooms, and an atmosphere of harmony prevails throughout the organization as this diary starts on Monday.

DECEMBER 2, 1935. This morning I was awakened by the night watchman, who told me that one of the stallions was sick and looked pretty dull. Hastily donning plenty of clothes, for it has been quite cold these last few nights, I repaired to the stallions' quarters where I found the teaser, a Thoroughbred horse, all stiff and humped up. He did not look at his feed, nor, contrary to his general practice, did he look at the mares as they went out for the day. Investigation proved that he had done a lot of running in yesterday's cold wind and had stood around outside all night, thus acquiring a cold in the lumbar regions which stiffened him up pretty well. Haarlem oil for the kidneys, a brisk rub over the affected area with the old-fashioned white liniment, a blanket, and a physic ball were his routine for the day. Our stallions at this farm run out as they please night or day, but usually have enough sense to come inside when the weather is bad. They see mares all round them and are quite often brought out for show, thus are not worried at all about what goes on around their quarters.

DECEMBER 3. The ground was frozen this morning but it was a bright clear day, so we spent much of the day hauling manure from the stables and spreading it thickly around the water troughs in the paddocks where the mares are. The troughs have to be bailed out every evening when the weather is cold and a good deal of ice and frozen mud makes it hazardous for the in-foal mares, so we lessen the danger of falls by putting the straw about. A few loads will be put in the gateways for better footing when leading the mares in and out after the troughs are taken care of.

DECEMBER 4. With the thermometer standing at 23 degrees and a strong west wind blowing, it has been very unpleasant today. The sun shone, however, and the stock seemed well satisfied when turned out. They seem to get colder standing inside than they do outside, where they can keep moving around.

The teaser has quite recovered and will go out tomorrow.

DECEMBER 5. It has been quite a lot warmer today, and the veterinarian has been here to operate on five of the yearling colts which were selected for castration. Our vet is a skilful chap, and a good horseman with it, so little time was lost performing the operation. In fact, he was only on the place an hour or so. By his method there does not seem to be much waste motion. A rope is plaited into the colt's tail and passed over the partition into the next stall, where it is held by two good men, a twitch having been put on the colt's nose meanwhile. One man stands at the colt's head and one stands to hand the doctor his instruments. The scrotum is thoroughly disinfected. The doctor then takes one organ in the left hand and with his knife makes a bold incision through which he draws the testicle. Holding the latter in the left hand, he next applies the emasculator for a couple of minutes. The instrument crushes the cord and the organ is ready to come out. The operation is repeated with the other organ, and finally the incisions are well washed with a disinfectant solution and the animal turned loose. Those operated on today behaved well, showing good spirit and paying little heed, all of them eating up their suppers in good shape. They will be stiff tomorrow, though.

DECEMBER 6. The castrated colts have apparently started on the road to recovery all right, for I saw them being led around the ring for an hour or so today in the bright sunshine and none seemed the worse for the operation. The incisions, of course, will be kept open so that the wounds may heal from the bottom.

The corn, a fine lot of big-eared yellow grain, has all been husked and has been stored adjacent to the various departments where it will be used. The farm stock get it all the time, and so do the barren mares, while mares in foal get about half oats and half corn. The corn will be discontinued a month or so before the mares should foal, and oats and bran will be fed exclusively. While on the mare subject, the annual guessing game is now on as to which of the few doubtful mares are in foal. We do not, at Sleepy Hollow Stud, examine all our mares as a routine matter as is done nowadays at so many studs, feeling that there is little to be gained by so doing under our particular set-up. Of course, if a mare is to be sold, or if there is doubt of a mare's physical condition, she is examined. I suppose it is largely a question of opinion whether it should be done or not, nevertheless, close check on a decade's breeding operations shows a percentage of in-foal mares running over 75, and that with an average of 50 mares bred a year.

DECEMBER 8. A cold, driving rain has kept horse and man indoors today. The mares quietly stand around chewing hay or looking out over the dreary aspect from their half-doors. The stallions seem to resent their confinement, which is necessitated by the rain driving into their stalls if the back doors are left open. The weanlings are feeling good, jumping around in their stalls and anxious to get out. When such weather lasts more than a day or two the feed will be cut down accordingly. The mares and saddle horses in the open seem to care little for the elements, for, apart from going into the shed for feed, they have been foraging around all day.

DECEMBER 9. At the training barn this morning I was reminded of the famous poem entitled *The Lay of the Hospital Race,* by "Hek," wherein the horses came out with "the ragged silks aloft and the odor of drugs astern." The odor of strong iodine paint and Irish reducine, the latter the more pleasant of the two, assailed my nostrils as soon as I walked in the doors of the training barn, and I knew at once that the annual fall leg-reclamation program had commenced. This year there are only yearlings at home, so there were no cripples, but it is considered by many a wise precaution, as it is by our trainer, to blister the knees or ankles of the yearlings when they are through training for the year. Some are blistered in both places and some get the paint and others the reducine. Either apparently is good, the latter being preferred when the animals are to be turned out to exercise.

The colts which were castrated, or rather, I should say, the geldings, have done fine. They were having daily exercise under saddle when I saw them, and are walked in the evening as well.

DECEMBER 10. Last night I was comfortably ensconced by the fire with the latest horse papers and a good-going pipe when the telephone called me to the training quarters again. A colt was in extremis with colic and all the colic mixture he had had could not do him any good. He had been washed out as a matter of regular routine but so much was he rolling around that it was feared that he would twist a gut. Sleep seemed indicated, and inducement in the shape of chloral hydrate capsules (two of them) being offered and more or less reluctantly accepted, sleep overcame the colt, which dreamed peacefully for a long time, awaking feeling very chipper. This happened to one of the best of the colts, as usual, and of course it happened on one of those cold nights when one appreciates the fireside.

DECEMBER 12. A balmy day with a hint of rain in the offing offered a good chance today to haul bedding into the open shed where are now 12 head of varied stock, barren mares, maidens, ponies, and so on. Three interested visitors from the frozen Northland blew in to inspect the stallions and stayed long enough to see everything. There is nothing like having interested visitors to make one enjoy showing one's stock and it is one of the chief pleasures of those horsemen whose work confines them to the farms to have people come and see the stock. Our men here are always impressed, when first hired, with the necessity for courtesy to all visitors at all times, regardless of the visitors' apparent walk of life. What a nasty taste is in one's mouth as one leaves the farm where one has been churlishly treated. Fortunately such farms are few and far between.

DECEMBER 13.   The threatened rain is here, in a deluge, and everything is inside, so the blacksmith takes this opportunity of going over all the mares' feet and shoeing a few, trimming some and cutting out the pockets which encourage the starting of thrush through holding the dirt, instead of letting it drop out as they move along. The men are taking the halters off the mares and are washing them in warm water and soda to get the old filth off them, following that with a going over with neatsfoot oil, applied with a rag when they are dry.   This routine makes the halters last longer and sometimes shows up where a mare is being chafed by an ill-fitting halter. Also, one can see stitching coming undone and can take the proverbial "stitch in time."

DECEMBER 14.   Today was chiefly spent in checking over the bloodlines of the mares booked to our two stallions and considering once more the matings of our own mares.   The factors of disposition and temperament are closely watched, as well as that of conformation.

DECEMBER 15.   Another wet Sunday, with everything indoors.   After a few hours with the Sunday papers I spent a couple more going from stall to stall contemplating the looks of the mares, weanlings, etc.   This is a good occupation for a wet Sunday, for one has ample opportunity for an unhurried inspection and often will note things about a mare which had escaped notice.   As the weanlings grow older they seem to change in various ways, and the fascinating study of conformation is always interesting.

DECEMBER 16.   The rain ceased during the night and the horses are all out again today, but the men have a big job mucking out the stalls. We do not clean out on Sundays at any time, nor do we do any work on the day of rest that is not essential, and a wet Sunday has to be paid for the next day.   All the wet bedding is removed and dry straw is piled along the walls of the stall and all damp spots are liberally treated with hydrated lime which does the double duty of a disinfectant and deodorizer while drying up the stall at the same time. The stalls are left open to the air until afternoon, when they are shaken down and fresh straw added wherever indicated. We do not bed the mares down very deeply, but they appreciate enough under them these cold nights, and they like a dry bed, however light.

DECEMBER 17. The gravel roads have been put in shape by the farm crew and all bad spots filled with fresh gravel and today the men are putting up snow fence where the drifts will form when we have our annual snow storms. At first blush this may seem a waste of money, but when the expense of such permanent improvements is balanced against the expense of digging out a couple of miles of road drifted three or four feet deep and entailing the hiring of a large temporary crew of men, it looks a good investment.

DECEMBER 18. The Aberdeen-Angus steers have been apportioned to the different departments of the farm where the most manure is made. The stable manure is daily hauled down to the well protected large corral where the steers feed on the refuse hay and trample the manure down, making it really worth something when the time comes to apply it to the fields. In this way no fresh manure goes on the land. Today we hauled a few loads of corn fodder to the corral to help along the feed.

DECEMBER 19. A very hectic day. Anyone who takes a day off to take the family Christmas shopping will realize the accuracy of the description. While in town took time off to visit a movie and to admire the wonderful acting of Charles Laughton in *Mutiny on the Bounty*. In the local newspaper office the talk was of the handicapping of the horses in the Santa Anita Handicap and it was a close decision as to whether the handicapper or the starter came in for the more cussing.

DECEMBER 20. Up at the training barn this morning for a visit with the trainer, whom I found watching his yearlings, now free of the troubles of training, enjoying their liberty in the paddocks where they spend a large part of each day. Watching the gambols and impromptu races staged, the trainer remarked that it simplified his work to no small degree when he had horses to train which had been used to running in big bunches. When that was the case, he remarked, the youngsters soon learned to take care of themselves in a crowd and got used to the crowding and bumping they would afterwards meet in real racing. Horses raised in single paddocks, or on farms where there were only one or two foals annually, take much longer to get used to horses hitting them and clods of dirt smacking them in the eye.

DECEMBER 21. A good hunting day with scenting conditions just right brought out a good crowd at our small local meet today. A score and a half of riders on all manner of beasts followed the 10 couples of foxhounds to covert where a red fox was soon put up and gave the field a merry chase for a few miles. One noted prevalence of the Thoroughbred blood present in the horses, several being clean bred. My own mount, a western three-quarter-bred of very mature years, cannot stick for very long with the clean-bred ones at the gallop but when it comes to sureness of foot and handy moving about, the years as an officer's mount tell, and I am well satisfied.

DECEMBER 22. Snow, snow, snow, all day, big, soft flakes that stay—and with the ground frozen underneath it looks as though there will be a white Christmas for a change. For the third consecutive Sunday the horses have been indoors, so all there is to do is to spend the time after the Sunday papers are exhausted in rummaging through the stud books and similar light literature. It is astonishing how interested one can become in one of these more or less dry publications. One will start out looking for some mare or foal's breeding and while turning the pages will be attracted by some familiar name or will see something of interest that one was not sure of, and it may be a long time before one finds the thing originally looked for.

DECEMBER 23. The snow stopped during the night, leaving about a four-inch spread blanketing the countryside. The mares and weanlings were soon gamboling about in it. It is amusing to see the actions of the little ones when they get their first snow bath. Snow is a great foot healer and many a foundered horse has been cured by turning him out in it. The youngsters were clamoring for a sleigh ride, and since it appeared much easier to do the job mounted, The Major, veteran of many a combat, was put to use and I mounted him bareback, except for the blanket, with a shank attached to the sleigh and held in one hand, to the great delight of the youngsters who have their times' love of speed and enjoy the old horse's fast trot down the road.

DECEMBER 24. Christmas Eve and the work was got through in good order by noon with a half-holiday for all to attend to their own affairs, aided by the pay check which came a week ahead of time. It snowed again last night, and with a dropping thermometer the snow will stay. All the stock was out today and appeared to thrive in the going. At some farms it is customary to feed hay outside in the pastures when there is snow on the ground, but here we almost never do it. If the snow is not too deep the mares will get more exercise foraging around and pawing through to get the last taste of green left by the season now gone. I saw a mare doing just that right by a pile of nice hay put out for her benefit a couple of days ago on a nearby farm.

DECEMBER 25. Christmas Day, a lovely morning with a crisp tang in the air and the sun brilliant on snow-covered fields. Up early, for well understood reasons, I drove around the farm and found all the men on the job and saw the stock turned out, all in good order and glad to be at liberty. The good weather did not survive the nooning and in the afternoon there was a blinding blizzard in full cry, with the drifts piling high about the yards. I believe the absolute zero of activities on the average stud is that period between Christmas and the New Year, for there is a holiday spirit prevailing and it is a good thing there is little to do, for no one feels much like doing.

DECEMBER 26. Today the snow-plows were out on the farm roads so that we could get about a bit. The thermometer plummeted about 25 degrees in 24 hours and at breakfast time the mercury stood at 6 above zero. The horses were not turned out until mid-morning and were put up by mid-afternoon, but foraged around and appeared well satisfied. There is no doubt that the exercise is better for them than standing indoors. There are no heated stables around this farm and consequently little sickness from changing temperatures. All a horse wants is comfort, for he is a hardy animal when given the chance to be. I sometimes think we pamper Thoroughbreds a bit too much.

DECEMBER 27. Another bitter cold day. The English papers came to hand today and it was interesting to scan the reports of the annual Newmarket December Sales. There is no doubt that the mare market is steadily improving everywhere. I noted that Jim Parkinson was buying a large number of mares and also stallions of all sorts for the Russians, in whose country bloodstock has sadly fallen off in number since the pre-war days when many a good horse, Derby winners included, went to the land of the Romanoffs. Jim Russell was buying for the South African market and the ever busy

British Bloodstock Agency got their usual large quota for all over the globe. Just how many were coming here I could not figure out.

DECEMBER 28. The third heavy snow to fall here in 10 days started this morning, and it is blowing very hard, to make things more interesting. With the wind in the northeast, it was good for all day and then some. Nothing out today, and all we could do was give them plenty of hay and water and go lightly on the grain ration. A good opportunity to write some of those neglected letters which are so hard to start.

DECEMBER 29. Not a blue Monday, but surely a white one. No roads open, and the two men who live off the place struggled through about 9 a.m., reporting the drifts deepening everywhere. One of these men has been here for well over 20 years and occupies a niche of his own in our structure. One of the best of the old type of negro, Jim is a man who can ever be depended upon, whatever the emergency, and I have often noticed how quickly he can outthink a horse. We have quite a number of these local men who have been on the place for years and have developed with it; they are invaluable.

DECEMBER 30. Clear and cold. The roads are opened again and the horses turned out today. They are glad to get a chance to run about a bit. The crust on the snow is not enough to cut their fetlocks, as sometimes happens. I noticed today that there were hundreds of birds hanging around the stables and house, so we are going around scattering granary sweepings on the frozen snow so that the birds may not starve.

DECEMBER 31. With the moderating weather all available help is shoveling the snow to the sides of the roads and digging us out. The steers were all inspected closely today and seemed to be thriving. It is remarkable how little they need besides the refuse bedding from the barns and some fodder. It has been a job to keep their water from being ice, so we are experimenting with a heater like those I have seen used out West in the severe winters to keep the troughs clear of ice. Two trainers en route to Hot Springs dropped in to see our young stock today and to see if we had anything for sale, cheap, of course, but as we had not, the youngsters came in for some favorable comment and the fortunate ones headed for warmer climes were on their way.

JANUARY 1, 1936. Waited up with a few friends to see the New Year in, and after about two hours sleep was awakened by the heavy feet of the watchman in the kitchen downstairs, not to wish us a seasonal greeting, however, but to inform me that one of our young mares appeared to have a pretty bad bout of colic. This at 3:30 a.m. Hastily slipping into enough clothes for Admiral Byrd, I went to the big enclosed barn housing the mares which will not foal very early and found the mare in question rolling and grunting about her condition. I at once gave her a good dose of standard colic mixture, and, knowing this patient well, a capsule of aromatic spirits of ammonia. This particular mare was raised here and went to the races to garner for us over a dozen purses. Not a high-class mare, she was yet one endowed with great courage and speed, and is now carrying her second foal. In half an hour the colic mixture was repeated and as the patient was getting eased up I returned to bed, though not without misgivings about her, for she has been having these attacks for five years now, and no doubt will have one too many one of these days.

JANUARY 2. The New Year's activity now commences and we can begin to prepare, first for the foaling season, and then for the covering season. Today the men have been busy catching up slack ends from the holidays and getting the barns in good order again while the horses are romping in the slowly melting snow. I have had the breeding tackle out for inspection to see what repairs are needed. We use simple things here and have not used a set of hobbles in a decade, preferring to use the twitch and figure-8 leg strap. We sometimes use a nose-rope on the mares but the most important thing of all is that we use a good man to hold the mares. I find we will have to order a set of new derby bandages which we use for tail protection, a clean one for each of the mares, so this is attended to. The rest of the equipment will be oiled up tomorrow.

JANUARY 3. Today we had the barren and maiden mares all brought in for examination. The maiden mares, ponies, etc., were turned right out as soon as the blacksmith had passed on their feet, while the barren mares came out one at a time for genital examination. There is not one of them that did not have a foal last year and examination failed to show anything in the half dozen to indicate cause for worry, so after treatment they are turned out.

JANUARY 5. A bright sunny day, and as all was well with the horses I loaded the family in the car and we set off to inspect some of the stallions and yearlings within a 50-mile radius. It seems strange to speak of yearlings again, but they all have birthdays on January 1. I have often thought that if such a date as, say March 1, could be set as the birthday we would be a great deal better off, for our foals would be coming at a natural time. No doubt the winter tracks would not like it but that the breed would be the better there would be few to deny. On today's trip I saw a goodly number of yearlings which appeared to be a better than average crop. I heard from several stallion owners the welcome news that the cash service question seems to be on the improve.

JANUARY 6. Deluges of rain today helped clear away the snow, of which little now remains to be seen. As the horses were all indoors the blacksmith went over their feet, trimming a little here, shoeing one there, etc. The snow has left them all in good shape and he had little to do to them. Up at the training stable the easy-going air of winter is being thrown off, and I saw the trainer and his helpers getting the tack out and in readiness for starting the horses out under saddle.

JANUARY 7. Up at the training quarters early this morning, expecting to see a few of the boys "buy a lot," as we say when one falls off, but nothing of the kind occurred. There are 20 2-year-olds up there and 17 of them started their preparation for the serious business of their lives this morning. They were carefully saddled up in the stalls and the boys put up inside. Led to the ring, they were walked about three times around the stable and then trotted, or jogged, seven times around. Our stable is enclosed only on the north side and has a single row of 30 stalls, facing the south, with the stalls divided into two blocks of fifteen each by an alleyway leading to the office and tack-room behind. The seven laps of the ring equal about 1⅛ miles. The footing is beach sand, which we find to be more practical than tanbark, as it does not freeze.

JANUARY 8. As the day was calm and dry, the farm staff took the opportunity to haul hay from some of the barns which will have a surplus to those which are getting short on hay. If this is done now we will not be running out in a blizzard, as once happened to us, causing the horse department to get cussed out, and rightly, by the farm gang. At Sleepy Hollow Stud we are happily situated in this respect, for the estate is departmentized under one general manager, each head being responsible for his own division, his help, and his results, and all pull together amicably for the common weal.

JANUARY 9. The steers came in for some attention today, being inspected by a cattle expert who was interested in our system of keeping them in the corrals and hauling our stable manure to them. The beasts were pronounced in excellent physical shape. The men have hauled a reserve of fodder down to them for use in bad weather, the last spell having used up all we had handy. The barren mares were gone over again today, three were treated a little, and two more had their shoes reset. I suppose some people think it foolish to shoe mares, but it has been our experience that if the front feet are shod the animals may be kept with less trouble, for a sore-footed mare will not forage like a sound one. Of course, some mares never have been shod, thus getting the tough hoof nature originally ordained for them.

JANUARY 10. It is surprising at times how the little ones grow so fast. Today we have been changing some halters on the yearlings, taking off the foal halters and putting on small yearling halters. These we have made for us of plain strong leather and having only one place to adjust them, that being the strap over the head. We have found that those halters having buckles on the nose-pieces, or on the chin pieces, or under the throat are very apt to be pulled open when the youngsters play in the paddocks and are frequently lost. A halter made with a reasonably small nose size and with a long enough headpiece does the job very well and few are lost. It was a dull, miserable, chilly day. Horses all out for the majority of the day but one could notice them seeking the more protected stretches of their pastures. The 2-year-olds seem to be settling down to their steady jogging nicely; they will keep up their seven times round the shed at the trot for a couple of weeks or so yet. One notes that things are tightening up all round and everyone is getting right into the collar for the fast approaching season. In the office they have been trying to find names for the few 2-year-olds which still remain unnamed. In spite of fullest cooperation by Registrar Klees it is an awful job to get horses named.

JANUARY 11. Damp and rainy again. Having a

cold today I have not been outdoors but have contented myself with the new Stallion Register checking up on the size of the sires registered therein. It is interesting to note that of the 117 horses listed, two are only 15 hands, Islam and his sire The Porter, 10 range from 15 to 15.2, 56 are between 15.2 and 16, and 39 vary from 16 to 16.2. Of the real big horses, over 16.2, there are but seven, with Gallant Sir tops at 16.3¾. *Dear Herod, Big Brand and Judge Hay at 16.3 are next in size. It is obvious therefore that the average size of the best American sires, which list includes Pennant, Display, Equipoise, *Chicle, Blue Larkspur and his sire Black Servant and his sire Black Toney, is between 15.2 and 16 hands, an answer for those who crave immense size which is hard to beat.

JANUARY 12. We had rather an interesting visitor at this stud today, the gentleman in question being Pat Horgan, racing secretary for the very successful Walter O'Hara of Narragansett Park. Mr. Horgan is touring the breeding farms and winter quarters in the interest of the New England Futurity and is getting personally acquainted with the breeders and farm managers who provide the material with which he has to work. He is also getting a load of the farm troubles poured into his ears and he tells me everyone is giving him the devil because he does not provide more filly races. He is going to try to do what he can to remedy this situation this year in New England and tells me Mr. O'Hara is like-minded.

JANUARY 13. Quite an interesting experiment was started here today. We have for some time now been trying to cure one of those rare cases of foot-canker in a 2-year-old and with the use of radium it appears as though he is getting along well. The bacteriologists from an important local institution have taken scrapings from the infected portions of the colt's foot, on which scrapings three different bacilli have been found and cultures made from them. These cultures, if that is the right term, were today put into the feet of a healthy animal in the hope that something might be learned which would show whether it was one of these bugs which caused the canker. Little enough seems to be known about the disease and the results of the experiment will be watched with interest. The subject of the experiment, a barren mare, had her feet anaesthetised with novocaine and the stuff was poured into holes cut into the crevices between the frog and sole of the foot, the holes being packed and the mare receiving a shot of tetanus serum to boot.

JANUARY 14. After looking over all the horses on the farm today I took to the road with the intention of seeing as many farms and horses as was possible in a three-day drive. It is my belief that anyone who is kept on a farm the most of his time owes it to himself and to his job, to get away once a year to look at other people's horses in order that he may not get too exalted an opinion of his own. It is my experience that I have never visited a farm—and I have never missed a chance of visiting one—that I did not learn something, either something of value or something not to do. Another thing is that by breaking away once in a while from the regular grind one is able to give better attention to one's job when one returns to it.

JANUARY 15. A pouring wet day but still on the road and visiting half a dozen farms, as well as covering a couple of hundred miles of good roads. Saw a great number of nice yearlings, the crop all in all appearing to be above the average, this estimate arrived at after inspecting some five hundred of the foals of 1935. A preponderance of fillies was noticeable and the breeders' bugaboo of what to do with them was frequently heard.

JANUARY 16. Arriving home this evening, I stopped off at the upper farm to have a look at the barren mare which was subjected to the injections of cultures last Monday. There seemed to be a definite reaction in one foot, though it is too early yet to tell just what sort of infection is there, whether it is from the bugs or the incision. We shall know something in a day or two now.

JANUARY 17. A fine day, with the raw feel of snow in the air. Today I have carefully inspected all the animals in the stud, appraising them in comparison with the hundreds seen in recent days. I have reached the conclusion that they compare favorably with those inspected elsewhere. The yearlings seem to have grown fast. It is always so when one is used to seeing them daily and then does not see them for some days. The in-foal mares are becoming very sedate as foaling time approaches. It looks as though there will be a foal in a couple of weeks. The barren mares are wintering well. They are rough and rugged and in fair flesh, with enough covering on their ribs, but not much fat. The stallions have been shod all round for their road work, which commences in a couple of days. The mares which will foal first are now getting oats and bran entirely, instead of corn.

JANUARY 18. After we had everything turned out this morning a heavy rain commenced and all hands got a ducking getting the horses in again. We do not like our mares heavy in foal to stand out in the winter rains, particularly if the rains are cold ones. I went up to the training quarters to watch the 2-year-olds getting their exercise. It is lengthened out a trifle now to eight turns of the shed at a good swinging trot. The youngsters seem to be getting legged up all right and are shaping up as we should wish them to.

JANUARY 19. This morning it was raining heavily from the nor'east, indicating we are in for a good one. The thermometer was at 32 degrees all day, so that the rain froze as it landed. The trees and everything were beautiful, but the roads were terrible. I have just come in from my evening inspection of the mares. They were standing quietly in their stalls, some chewing hay, but the majority merely loafing, and it was quite a scene within doors. The yearlings were moving about a good deal, resenting their enforced captivity. The rain is turning to snow and the radio tells us that we are in for a deep one. The mare whose foot was injected with the bugs is very sore on it, and there is an unpleasant-smelling discharge from it. At the barren mare shed all of the bunch is inside for once. I watched them fed and saw them all plod through the rain to the artesian well with its ground-level trough where they get their water. These wells are invaluable where there is no natural flow of water.

JANUARY 20. It was a lovely morning, with the sun reflected from millions of icicles on trees, grass, fences, everything. We had to hold up on turning out until almost noon on account, of the icy condition of the yards, but the ice soon softened on top. The mare whose foal is first expected has been put at the end of the row of foaling stalls and the other mares have been put in according to their due dates, not that they are at all likely to pay close attention to their dates. I have always considered foaling dates as merely a guide to probabilities, although some people get unduly alarmed if a mare does not foal by the clock and calendar. A good motto was taught me years ago by an old negro stud groom: "When peaches are ripe, they'll fall."

JANUARY 21. The doctors were at the upper farm today and took swabs from the injected mare's foot. Infection of some sort is developing and they are anxious to find what they can get from her foot. There was plenty of action going on when I stopped by the training department, with the 2-year-olds getting a few turns of the shed at a good rousing gallop. They like this, and it is a welcome change from the steady

jogging. I watched a big Hi-Jack colt go bucking down one side like a broncho, but the boy
stayed with him. Our trainer insists that the
lads use a good long stirrup, for he rightly insists that with their knees under their chins too
many boys get thrown and hurt in shed work.

JANUARY 22. A grand day, with everything
out enjoying it. Plenty of fresh air and sunshine, the great germicide, is invaluable this
time of the year. The mare due tomorrow is
getting very sluggish but will be a few days yet.

JANUARY 23. What a day! Last night at 10
o'clock it was 37 on my thermometer and
when I got up this morning it was two degrees
below zero, with a howling gale from the northwest to make things more interesting. The
electric pump, 10 feet below ground in a pit,
froze up, though a coal oil stove soon fixed that.
No horses out all day and everything shut up
tight with plenty of hay and good beds.

JANUARY 24. It had warmed up to four above
this morning, but the wind was still strong.
Nothing went out but the 2-year-olds, which enjoyed their galloping around the shed at the
training barn. It is interesting to watch them
shape up and it will not be long before the big
middles of wintertime will be disappearing. They
do not take much cooling out this weather. The
boys have taken strips of old coolers to wrap
around their ears and lower faces and they look
weird as they gallop around. No sooner are they
off than there is a concerted rush to the stove
while the men get the horses ready for walking.
The weather seems to suit the animals, though.
Horses and cattle are thriving.

JANUARY 25. With the thermometer rising we
are able to turn everything out for exercise today,
though they cannot be out too long for the
frozen ground is so rough that they will not do
much running on it. The in-foal mares move
around with great dignity, conscious, perhaps, of

their impending importance. The mare due today is shaping up slowly but looks good for three or four days yet; we are hoping it gets warmer before she does foal.

JANUARY 26. Horses all out all day in pleasanter weather conditions. How deep the frost is in the ground was shown this morning when it was found that the pipes, at least a foot and a half below the ground were frozen in many exposed places, necessitating the using of water tubs which can be carried from the stables in the smaller paddocks. We are most thankful for the artesian well which never gives the trouble the other system does and gives water of better temperature. In summer the artesian water is always cool, in winter it is never as cold as the water that lies in the troughs a while.

JANUARY 27. A 15-degree drop in the mercury again, with the strong wind giving us more of this zero business. All stock indoors again and all doing well. From California today comes a letter from a reader of this diary who asks me whether I would breed a mare which had slipped at seven months and whether this misfortune is apt to occur again next year. Also he asks what procedure we would follow in such a case. There are many causes for a mare to slip her foal; comparatively few slips are caused by the abortion germ. Nevertheless it is always wise to send the expelled foetus and a blood sample to a laboratory for examination. Have a competent vet take smears also and send them in for culturing. Mares will often slip twins, which I regard as a darn good thing. A mare may be kicked in pasture, causing abortion. Regarding a repetition; I should hesitate to answer and would advise a thorough physical examination by the vet. Personally, if I have such a mare, I like to wait until the warm sun and the springtime grasses have toned her up, not breeding her before mid-April at the earliest.

JANUARY 28. Warmer again and all the horses out for a few hours sunning. We should have a foal in a day or so now; the mare which is over-due has some wax on the teat-ends, but only a little, nor are these organs as distended as usual at foaling. This mare had a few hours outside in a paddock where she could be watched. It is not wise to let such mares get out of sight in a big field for they may foal in short order and get into trouble unknown to anyone.

JANUARY 29. Sunny and pleasant, but with more snow promised. At the upper farm we have rigged up a pair of stocks for shoeing such of the mules and work stock as resent this neces-sary attention. One big mule was in them this afternoon when I was up there and in spite of plenty of trying he was unable to do anything about it and finally submitted to the attentions of the farrier. All the work stock is being shod, as they have some road work to do and if not shod their feet will last but a short time on the frozen gravel roads.

JANUARY 30. At last we have a foal, a filly, of course, but a good one. The dam had shown uneasiness during the afternoon, so was stabled early, but settled down and fed up. At almost midnight the watchman informed me that foaling would not be long, so out I went to find her down and in a few minutes all was over. Under our routine for the foaling season, the watchman keeps close watch on all mares when close up and notifies me at once when he sees the mare getting uneasy. When the mare goes down we have learned to let her alone until it appears absolutely necessary to help her out. If it does become necessary, we take a firm hold on the fore legs and pull, steadily and downwards, towards the hocks, but only as she strains herself. As a rule it takes but a few minutes. When the foal is out and gulping breath we pull him right around to the mare's head so she may see him and lick him dry. The navel is well dusted with a good drying powder

which we have satisfied ourselves to be the best
for the job. Should it bleed much it is tied up
with sterile gauze stripping, but this seldom
is necessary. As the mare lies all wet bedding
is removed, and when she gets up the remainder
that she had lain on comes out, and the damp
spots are raked up and lime spread on them.
Plenty of dry, clean bedding is then put in, a
fresh bucket of water and a forkful of alfalfa
also. In cold weather the foal should be rubbed
dry with plenty of straw at once, as circulation
is thereby aided. Fortunately last night was
comparatively a warm one.

JANUARY 31. The foal was racing around the
stall, kicking up high when I went out this
morning, so she is going the right way. It is
very cold again but the little one minds it not
at all. Had she been born tonight I should have
had to put a little blanket on her. All horses in
today, a gale blowing.

FEBRUARY 1. Today we had to remove our lot
of steers at the stud farm to the field where
the barren mares run out and where the Madden
shed is, for the water pipes, two feet below the
ground, are frozen up. Up there they have the
invaluable artesian well for water supply. They
will run with the horses in the shed and will not
need much extra attention. All horses out today.

FEBRUARY 2. A pleasant Sunday morning. As
everything was out I took the opportunity of
saddling my horse and riding through the fields
to look the horses over out of doors and thus
spent a pleasant leisurely three hours. All appeared well content and thriving. It appears as
though we shall have quite a wait for our next
foal, and I am glad of it, things being as they
are. After lunch I took the mare and foal out
in the yard for some sunbathing out of the wind.
The filly did not care to follow at once and had
to be coaxed from behind a trifle at first, but
she soon was running around her anxious dam
as I held the latter on the shank. We try to

get the little ones out for a short time each pleasant day when the sun's rays are strongest.

FEBRUARY 3. A fair day, so everything went out early, only to be quickly returned indoors when a swift-falling snowstorm came on quite unexpectedly. The blacksmith spent the remainder of the day trimming the feet of the yearlings. This time, in view of the rough frozen ground, he did not take much off the feet, merely rounding the edges in order that there should be no breaking them off

FEBRUARY 4. With everything covered with a half-inch or more of ice, we were able to do little today. A small halter was put on the foal and she was led about her stall a little by hand. We halter the foals early and teach them to stand tied as soon as they are old enough. It is much easier to handle a week-old foal than one a month old. While it is often customary not to bother with these things until they have to be done, yet the path of least resistance is to get it over early.

FEBRUARY 5. This morning we laid down straw walks for the mares from the stables to the paddock gates, for, while the footing in the fields was all right, the yard was ice-coated. All went out without event and will be the better for the outing. I watched the 2-year-olds getting their work at the training quarters today and was struck by the way they had shaped up since being put to work. The big middles are gone and the quarters and backs are filling out as they should. The youngsters today were getting their work on the reverse way of going. The trainer likes to change them from time to time in order to get them used to galloping on either lead and to develop them as well one way as the other. Also, when this is done a horse is not as apt to get a one-sided mouth.

FEBRUARY 6. A good day with not much ice around gave us a welcomed opportunity to haul feed to the several barns at the stud farm and corn to the shed barn. All feed comes to the granary at the upper farm. There it is in charge of one man, who issues it to each department as it is needed, and thus an accurate check of the costs of the feed used by each is kept. The filly foal has a little diarrhea this afternoon. This is to be expected when the mares come in season around the ninth day and usually does not last long. We will not breed the mare, although she is in good physical shape, as she is prone to foal ahead of time, and she might thus have another foal this year.

FEBRUARY 7. It is a good thing we replenished our supplies yesterday for we had today the heaviest snow of the winter, so far. I have just come in from making the 10 o'clock round with the night watchman and to see the full moon shining over the woods and unbroken snow of the big fields is a beautiful sight, but from the point of view of the working man, Sherman's famous opinion of war is applicable to the winter season.

FEBRUARY 8. Bright sunny days like today do a lot to compensate us for the bad days of the winter, for the horses all seem to feel as good as do we. When turned out in the snow, which is 10 inches deep on the flats, they kicked up and went off sailing. Noticing one of the barren mares down near the shed, we brought her in to the home stables where we treated her for a slight case of colic. She seems a trifle dull, so will remain here for a few days before returning to the shed. These occasional cases demonstrate the real necessity for constant inspection of all the stock. If left too long, bad complications often ensue, possibly causing loss of the animal.

FEBRUARY 9. Sunday, supposedly a day of rest but not so today. More snow last night caused the mules to work hard clearing the roads again, one man reported off sick, and the barren mares and steers decided to seek pastures new and crossed a broad sheet of ice and frozen snow into the farm manager's garden. It was a ticklish proposition to decide how to get them safely back, but one of the men wisely suggested leaving them alone until evening feeding time and then calling them back. As we have always taught our horses to come at a call, they soon came sailing across the ice and got back safely to the shed for their feed.

FEBRUARY 10. There is nothing, to my mind, like deep snow for showing up a horse's action. This was brought home to me this morning when, our stallion groom being off sick, I went down to turn out the two stallions kept at the home farm. As it snowed a little and blew from the northeast, their stalls were shut up last night, and when I opened the doors into the paddocks they went off sailing. New Arrival went out first, trotting straight out with action like a Hackney stallion in a show, and when I turned out Galloping Lad the two went up and down their respective fences showing off their paces in fine shape. A few minutes of this sufficed them, and, as though by design, both decided to take a snow roll at the same time.

FEBRUARY 11. A bitter cold day again. Today we had the smith go over all the mares' feet with his knife so that there should be no pockets for thrush to form. With the horses indoors so much and the difficulty of hauling out the manure as regularly as is customary, there is danger of this condition developing. Nothing out today, but the 2-year-olds are galloping strongly at the training quarters. They get about six rounds of the shed at a good gallop as well as a similar number of turns at the trot.

FEBRUARY 12. We have here an old pensioner, the first mare bred on this farm. She is about 25 now. A half-bred trotter, she was at one time a fine saddler, but now is used only for breeding, as she foals regularly. As her last year's foal would have been an odd member, we left her on the dam as long as we could to see what would happen and at last it looks as though we must wean her. The mare has a surprising quantity of milk but she is kicking the foal away from her quite a bit now, the latter having developed into a good saddle horse prospect while enjoying the dam's milk. I often wonder if we are so wise with our early weaning, and whether the mare is not a better judge of her foal's needs than is her owner.

FEBRUARY 13. Rain, sleet, snow, and ice-coated windshields combined to curtail activities today. The only brisk activity occurred when the stallion groom was found to have "an appendix"—something he does not have tonight. A good evening to catch up with reading and correspondence was not to be missed, and among other readings Dave Alexander's column in the *Morning Telegraph* is always good entertainment. For real pleasure I commend *Horse and Hound*.

FEBRUARY 14. Last night it rained steadily and today we have floods and a partial thaw, so the most of the day was spent in digging ditches to draw off water which was pouring into the stables and houses. At the upper farm I found men carrying water from that invaluable artesian well, as the engine and pump in the pit were under four feet of water when they came to work this morning. Only the stallions were out today, and they not for long. The young filly foal born recently is taking a tremendous amount of exercise, as she will gallop around her mildly protesting dam for 10 minutes at a stretch.

FEBRUARY 15. A good day overhead and a belated "January thaw" permitted all our horses to get the whole day outdoors and also afforded me an opportunity of getting a good long ride around the fields on horseback. The amount of snow and ice still covering everything is astonishing and if the thaw keeps on we shall certainly have danger of floods, as this country does not take the waters away fast. I found the horses all in fine order and from the vantage point of the back of The Major was able to consider them individually and collectively with small effort. It is interesting to note the difference in the development of the in-foal mares as their times draw close. Some have had many foals and show little wear and tear, still having the shape of very young mares. Others which have had but a foal or two look like old mares.

FEBRUARY 16.   Sunday again and dull and cheerless, the thaw still continuing to make vile conditions underfoot. There being little or no profit from sitting indoors, I succumbed to pressure and took the family visiting after church time. Combining my own pleasure with theirs, I was able to stop at a few places to look at horses but found everyone still winter-bound and very little activity forward anywhere.

FEBRUARY 17.   Today we took advantage of the moderated weather and gave the yearlings their second worming, over a month late due to the bad weather. They were fasted about 15 hours beforehand and their buckets of water were removed about three hours ahead of the operation, which consisted of giving them about half an ounce of carbon disulphide (U. S. P.) followed by about two ounces of water, through the stomach tube. Twenty-five head were treated and the veterinarian was not on the farm more than an hour and a half in all. Water was given again about an hour after treatment, followed by a feed of hay at night, and half a feed of grain will be given in the morning. The operation was performed without event, except that one colt disagreed about it but was soon shown the error of his ways and submitted meekly.

FEBRUARY 18.   Had a look at the youngsters first thing this morning and found them all fine. Only one or two had failed to clean up their feed. They will gradually be brought back to full feeding as their appetites show their requirements. I used to be averse to the tube on principle, but am now absolutely in favor of it, but, it must be used by a competent man and the size of the tube had better be small rather than large. An overlarge tube occasionally draws blood.

FEBRUARY 19. The yearlings which were wormed a couple of days ago are passing a good-ly number of parasites, chiefly the long round-worms (ascarids), though a few strongyles and an occasional bot have shown up. Curiously, some of those which to all appearances needed treating worst have shown up little, while one big strapping filly which is round as an apple and keeps well on next to nothing has passed more worms than I ever saw from a yearling. Thus one cannot always depend on outward appear-ance to guide one as to the need of treatment against parasites. It is a good thing that the treatment was done at the time it was, for last night we had a 27-degree drop in the tempera-ture, bringing it down near zero once more. With a strong northeast wind to freshen things up we have everything indoors today. The horses have spent more time inside than I ever saw them do in any previous winter.

FEBRUARY 20. Spent most of the morning at the training stable where I saw four sets of the 2-year-olds get their work. It was a most interesting morning, for I had not watched the whole lot for a long time. They are galloping now close on 2½ miles daily, besides a prelimi-nary trot of about half a mile. The lot of them are growing right and are full of vim, indicating that they are getting about what they need in the way of feed and work. The trainer considers his feed boxes the chief guide as to the work to be accomplished. I noticed that a good number had either ankle boots or polo boots on, these protecting the legs from self-inflicted blows. An-other thing about these boots is that a green rubber (groom) can put bandages on in such a way as to bow a horse's tendon and a green man can't go wrong strapping boots on.

FEBRUARY 21. The arrival of visiting mares

for the breeding season is beginning. Already
we have five visitors from away, so we are starting the teasing of the barren mares. The visiting
barren mares are kept at the upper farm until
such time as the weather is fit for them to go
out to the shed barn with the rest. The stallion
kept at the upper farm is used for this purpose
and he is led down the line of boxes every other
day and is allowed to visit with the mares over
the tops of the half doors. Down at the home
farm we commenced operations today, riding the
teaser up to the field in which is located the
Madden shed and letting him stand around the
fence while the mares and he got acquainted.
This will be done three times weekly all season
from now on.

FEBRUARY 22.   Starting cold, the weather
warmed into a nice afternoon, just right for a
brisk ride on a good mount. The fields being too
icy, I kept to the roads up to our local hunt club,
where a group of riders was gathered and on the
point of going out to exercise hounds. Joining
them I enjoyed a good ten-mile jaunt. Back by
dark through the now muddy fields.

FEBRUARY 23.   My Sunday morning sleep was
rudely disturbed at 3:30 a. m. by the night watchman charging in—the wire terrier nearly took
his leg off—to tell me that one of the best of
the mares was down, cast badly in a corner of
her stall. Rushing out with little on, I found
the mare had got her head down in a corner
where she had pawed all her bedding away to
get all the hay she could find. We quickly got
forks and pulled the bedding from under her
and slipped a shank over her off fore pastern, as
she was on her right side. Our united efforts
soon pulled her around and she jumped up,
sweating some and nervous to a degree.   To
quiet her I slipped her a chloral hydrate capsule
and she soon settled down to a small bunch of
alfalfa which we put into the stall to distract
her attention from her troubles.

FEBRUARY 24. Bred our first mare today. The belated breeding season is starting. The mare, a visitor, was examined and found to be in good shape. The tail was bandaged with a clean sterile bandage and she was led over to the stallion's stall where she was well tried over the half door. She was in good order, so she was taken into his paddock where the best footing was. The figure-8 leg strap was placed on her near foreleg and a twitch was put on her nose. The stallion was led out, quietly, and was allowed to approach her on the near side, where she could not have kicked him if she had tried. The cover was accomplished without any untoward event. The stallion was led back to his stall and then was turned out. The mare went right out into the paddock.

FEBRUARY 25. There was a real feeling of spring in the air this morning. The snow and ice are melting, and what a mess there is underfoot. We had the teaser up at the shed barn this morning. We have a coupe of men there to stop any kicking among the mares and to lead up for special attention any mares that seem to warrant it. In years of experience with this kind of trials I have found very few mares which did not indicate in some manner to a watchful observer the fact that they were not in season. This is nature's method and is following her lines much closer than if we were to take the mares into a pen and twitch them and otherwise disturb them. This teasing of the barren and maiden mares will be continued at least three times weekly throughout the entire season, so that none may be overlooked.

FEBRUARY 26. Just how much of a guide to probabilities the list of dates on which mares are due to foal is, was demonstrated to me today when I was checking the list which is placed on one of the stable walls for the benefit of the men. No less than five mares are overdue, from two to seven days and none of them seems to be in the least bit of a hurry about it.

FEBRUARY 27. A bright, warm day, with signs everywhere that the lethargy of winter is being thrown off. Today we had a couple of men going around on a wagon with planks, posts, nails, and all the incidentals needed. They had instructions to inspect fences closely, to repair all the boards loose, split, or lost, and to replace any posts which apparently need it. This has to be done from time to time and it is a good thing to get it done when there is nothing much else on hand. After breeding a mare this morning, I got a sample of the semen from the horse for examination under the microscope and was pleased to find it full of vigorous cells, or spermatozoa. We make a practice of examining the stallion's semen at regular intervals throughout the season, usually about twice a week.

FEBRUARY 28. A freeze came last night and one can again get about without rubber boots. The horses did not cut deep into the turf of their paddocks, as the surface was hard again. It is always a moot question with me in the spring, do we do more harm to the fields by turning the horses out, or to the mares and yearlings by keeping them up? Personally, I like to save the fields all that is possible, but believe the animals must get out, so out they go, and I suppose in a couple of months the fields will have recovered. This is the time of the year, by the way, to send the chain harrows over the pastures, whenever the footing is firm, so that the droppings may be scattered, that is, if they are not picked up, as is being done more and more on the big farms.

FEBRUARY 29. Another pleasant day, with everything out. The five overdue mares have a paddock to themselves today, hard by the barns, for, although none of them appears to be ready for foaling as yet, it does not take some of them long when they make up their minds. At the training stable I watched the 2-year-olds getting their long gallops, part of which were made at good speed. It will be a long time yet before they go on the track, for measurement shows that but six inches on the top of the ground is thawed out yet, and in many places there were thirty inches of frost.

MARCH 1. Frost again last night, but a pleasant sunny day saw everything in the fields all day except the mare and foal which had a short run in the sun this afternoon, much to the enjoyment of several visitors whom the pleasant day had brought out.

MARCH 2. Up at 1:30 a. m. to welcome another filly to our stud, her advent being accomplished without incident. Called to the upper farm this afternoon, where a yearling filly had picked up a nail in some manner. First aid measures were immediately taken. The nail was pulled out—it had gone into the point of the frog —and the hole was opened up with a small sharp knife and filled with crystals of resublimed iodine, on which was poured spirits of turpentine which set fire to the crystals, thus completely cauterizing the wound. The foot was then poulticed with a flaxseed poultice, very hot, and well covered up with sacking and a bandage, and the filly received a half-sized prophylactic dose of tetanus antitoxin. She will be kept under close observation but after such measures, quickly applied, there is not likely to be any further trouble.

MARCH 3. Another filly arrived here this morning, coming in rather a peculiar fashion. The dam, a husky young mare having her second foal, showed no desire whatever to lie down at all, nor has she done so as yet and the foal is nine hours old. The mare simply stood in one spot and with quick, straining jerks proceeded with the parturition. We left her alone until the foal's head was out and it was apparent that she had no intention of lying down. We helped her along then, and as the foal came out we had a pile of deep straw behind the dam to break the little one's fall. As she came out to the hips the night watchman held the foal in his arms and we gradually let her down, dusting the navel well as soon as the foal was on the straw. The mare cleansed in an hour or so and otherwise the operation was without incident. Why she objected to following the usual procedure of lying down is beyond me for she had been in the habit of lying down regularly at night, and she was not at all disturbed by anything we did.

MARCH 4. We have been blanketed with a thick fog most of today but this evening it cleared away nicely and the mares, which had been shapeless forms in the fog resumed their normal shapes. None of those close to foaling went out until it did clear, as it is too easy for them to slip out of sight and one can never depend too closely on what they will do. The filly whose foot picked up the nail is sound and well again. The hole will be kept picked out and plugged with oakum and tar, a small quantity being packed into it daily.

MARCH 5. Another filly arrived this morning, a first foal from a young mare who was bred right out of training. She is a little thing but finely made and she is not too strong. It is interesting to watch the mare getting around her first-born and the care she takes not to tread on her. The mare has a great deal of milk and we are having to draw some from her to ease the udder for the little one will not take it all yet, and the udder would become distended so that she would have difficulty in nursing if relief were not given. This foal arrived some 10 days ahead of time but we have three that are from five to 12 days overdue and this latter condition seems to be prevalent hereabouts this season. One old stud groom has told me he had noted that in severe winters when the mares did not get out much the foals usually were late in arriving.

MARCH 6. Today I tested the semen of the two stallions, as both were in use. This is a simple matter and it pays anyone with a stallion to test frequently during the season. All that is needed is to have the microscope—any sort of microscope will do—set up in readiness and as the stallion dismounts a few drops of semen can usually be caught in a warm bowl. Hurry this into the house where it is warm and put a drop or two on the slide and you can see how the spermatazoa are doing. There should be a large number of them and they should be active and swimming around vigorously. If they are not so it is best to consult a competent veterinarian for advice, but check from the next service first to make sure.

MARCH 7. The mares with foals get an additional light feed at mid-day as well as their morning and evening feeds. It is interesting to watch how quickly the foals learn to eat with their dams. We have two fillies now not a week old which are right in the box as soon as the feed is in. Our mares' stalls have wide, three cornered feed boxes which are two feet on each side and are five inches deep. They are bolted into the walls and are removable for cleaning. By having low-sided boxes the little ones can get at the feed without hurting their jaws and necks. The boxes are about two and a half feet from the floor.

MARCH 9. An important occasion was today for our 2-year-olds, for they were taken out onto the mile-long home track, for the first time this spring. The going was still deep in places but they went along in fine shape, feeling their oats and kicking up in fine style. It appeared as though there might be some loose horses at first but soon all settled down and did their work in a very creditable manner. They galloped a mile and a half today and will only gallop until the condition of the track warrants some faster work, which will not be long if this decent spring weather keeps on.

MARCH 10. Called out of bed at 1:00 a. m. by the watchman as one of the mares 15 days over-

due was about ready to foal. The foal arrived
in fine shape and there were joyful faces to see
a colt at last after four fillies, and what a colt!
A big, rugged, well boned bay lad with good
straight legs and up and nursing in less than
an hour. The old saying is that if a mare runs
overdue the foal will be a colt will be right in this
case, though according to the records kept here
for the last 10 seasons it's just as likely to be
the other way round.

MARCH 11.   As is usually the case in a late
season, when one mare comes in heat they all do,
and today we had five to one horse. The stallions are now making one cover daily six days
a week. Later, when they are fully fit, it will
be two a day, spaced at least 10 hours apart.
Microscopic examination today showed both of
them to be working well. We only breed at
Sleepy Hollow Stud on six days a week and on
Sundays our stallions get as complete a rest as
possible. This plan seems to work well and the
percentage of fertility has never been impaired
thereby.

MARCH 12.   For 30 hours the rain has poured
down.   It will at least penetrate through the
last of the deep frost and the land will have a
chance to settle when it does clear up. With all
horses indoors and thriving well there was little
to do. I got out the pedigrees of the mares and
of the stallions which they will be mated with
for this year, and figured out what bloodlines
we were blending and so on. This has been done
very often before but however much one cons
a pedigree it seems as though there is always
more to be noted about it when referred to again.
One foal seems sure to be here in a few hours
as the mare has refused her supper and has a
worried, restless look on her face. She stood
with her head on my shoulder for the past 10
minutes, telling me about it all.

MARCH 13.   I had no more than got well off to
sleep when the heavy tread of the night watch-

man resounded through the kitchen. After years of this subconscious waiting for a call, one rolls out of bed still asleep and into old pants and sweater, left handy nearby, without knowing it. Last night I found it out when hitting my head on the doorpost. The foal which arrived was a welcome one, a big rugged sort of colt, and as all was well with both mother and son an hour saw me back under the covers.

MARCH 14. A truly springlike day with the land drying out fast. The 2-year-olds were on the track for some good open gallops this morning and it was good to see them out again. Rode around looking at the crops here this afternoon and found the wheat and rye looking well and green. We are growing a lot of these grains as we will use all the straw next winter.

MARCH 15. Sunday again. One gets the work over with as soon as possible and the men, except the one whose turn of duty it happens to be, are off till evening stable time. The stallions seem to know that nothing is expected of them and they relax in their paddocks while the in-foal mares bunch up together in the spring sunshine. After a week of trying to catch up with the belated seasonal work it is good to stroll quietly around on Sunday and to take stock of the week's work and plan the next one. Spent an enjoyable afternoon showing the horse population of the farm to some of those keen appreciative visitors whom it is always a pleasure to entertain.

MARCH 16. More visiting mares arrived today and our facilities will soon be overtaxed if many more arrive before the barren mares can go out for good. At the stable the 2-year-olds galloped this morning in preparation for some swifter work tomorrow. If foaling mares and services permit, will go up and spend part of the morning there. The last of the water lines to the paddocks thawed out without bursting today so we are once more relieved of the trouble of

hauling from the stables to the smaller paddocks. The troughs received their regular bi-
weekly cleaning out today as they are back in
service again.

MARCH 17. St. Patrick's day with the fields
now rapidly turning to that saint's emerald hue.
Saw a set of 2-year-olds breeze up at the training stable this morning but as the track was
still heavy they only went three-eighths in about
43 seconds. All went well, however, and they will
be speeding up soon. Thinking the rains about
over we dragged the yards and roads at the stud
today, but a gale set in after nightfall with torrents of rain.

MARCH 18. The rain ceased this morning leaving floods everywhere. Today we have shipped
away two more mares which will visit stallions
away from home. The mares will stay at their
new locations for the rest of the season. One of
our five overdue mares, a maiden, has been running milk now for two days, which is quite ir-
regular but sometimes happens. She has been
kept up for close observation. Everyone seems
to be having mares overdue this season.

MARCH 19. Another wet day, with flood reports coming in. How any of the northern
trained horses are to be sharpened for speed this
year is a mystery. It looks as if the winter raced
ones will have all the edge. All horses indoors
today with the blacksmith going over their feet,
giving them whatever attention they need. The
mares which are very heavy in foal have their
feet only picked out; they will be shod again
after foaling. Having seen the mares fed for the
evening I came in and five minutes later was
called out again as another mare was foaling,
one I had just looked at. She merely stopped in
the midst of her feeding, had the filly, which she
carried, incidentally, but six days short of a full
year, and in 15 minutes was up finishing the
feed. Some nonchalance, that. Due to such a

long time in cramped quarters the filly will need some time to get herself straightened out.

MARCH 20. Another new arrival this morning, a nice colt too. Yesterday's filly was by the super-horse, Man o' War and today's colt is by the champion's greatest rival of 16 years ago, John P. Grier. These two youngsters can do some boasting about their respective daddies when they get together loafing in the paddock sunshine; maybe they'll be rivals as were their sires when their time comes. The 2-year-olds were getting a quarter-mile work when I stopped by their department this morning. It appears there might be some real runners among them.

MARCH 21. The rain pouring down in torrents has kept everything within doors again today. Withal the fields are getting greener. The foals are anxious to get out and give their mothers plenty to do at times following them about the stalls. Most of the day I have spent studying the *Bloodstock Breeders' Review,* which came to hand a few days ago. One wonders why our public does not support such a publication. Of great interest to me was the obvious stress laid on the value of fillies. Often they outsold the colts, for the Englishman's eye is on the possible stud career ahead. Is it any wonder that the English mares still supply the cream of the whole world's racing stock?

MARCH 22. The number of our filly foals has again reached the ratio of 2-1 with the colts. Another of the former came shortly before dawn this morning. The rain stopped during the night and strong winds will help to dry things up a bit. Why is it that so many mares foal between midnight on Saturday and Monday morning? I have watched this phenomenon with some curiosity for several years, keeping records on it for one or two seasons. Last year we had a foal arriving each Sabbath for several straight weeks. I wonder if the peculiar quietness which always seems to mark the day of rest is in some way responsible. The scientists would scoff at that.

MARCH 23. The 2-year-olds are breezing along three times a week; the farm crew is busy trimming up everywhere, awaiting the drying of the fields to get on with the sowing; and here at the stud we are as busy as can be with the breeding and trials of the mares. Today we had most of the foals out a while. As the ground is still very wet they are only out long enough to get some exercise and sunshine. If left out too long they will lie on the damp ground and are quite likely to get colds and possibly pneumonia.

MARCH 24. One of the older foals has a bad attack of diarrhea today. He is one of those gluttons which insist on eating as much and as fast as their dams, and is paying the penalty now. He has had an ounce of castor oil to clean out the cause of his trouble and tomorrow morning will be started on the regular diarrhea mixture. So far he is nursing well but if he slacks up the mare's udder will be kept slack so that no inflammation develops. While he is under the weather he will not go out at all, as he would be likely to get overheated.

MARCH 25. The parade of fillies keeps on. Midnight last night saw yet another arriving. Another good one but as usual a colt would have been somewhat more welcome. It is like Mark Twain said about the weather, "There's more said about it than done," and I don't suppose that science will ever get to the point that we will be able to predetermine sex in any species. It is better so, I expect. The foal with the diarrhea is much better tonight, following a good clean out from the castor oil. The stallions covered two mares each today and the semen showed up excellently on examination.

MARCH 26. This morning, after the regular daily trials of the mares and the morning breeding had been attended to I rode up to the training quarters to see the youngsters get their work. Today all were breezed three-eighths and the most of them went the distance around 41 seconds. They will be sent along for a good work again on Saturday. I returned through the field where the men are hauling the manure from the Madden shed. This is to be ploughed for ensilage corn for our Jersey herd. The manure is rich and well rotted, the shed having been bedded largely with the manure, which has a lot of straw in it from the mare barns.

MARCH 27. Shipped away a mare and foal by van today, the little fellow leading right up the runway nicely with the tailrope through his halter. The everlasting filly parade proved the old saw, about mares running overtime having colts, wrong again. Last night's chestnut filly, which the dam was kind enough to present us with right after supper, was carried 20 days longer than the eleven months usually allowed for such matters. Result—a foal very large and a somewhat bruised mare, I would much rather have the growing done on the outside of the dam; it's easier on the mare.

MARCH 28. Much too much water standing everywhere for the foals to go out, worse luck. Visiting the training stable I found five majestic wild geese, which had seemingly mistaken the infield of the track for a lake. They stayed on the ground for a few minutes while the horses cantered in their direction, then left with a great deal of adverse comment, which did nothing to help quiet the 2-year-olds.

MARCH 29. This having been a lovely day, there was a large crowd of visitors to see the foals. As there are a few mares here which were great favorites with race goers, they like to see the foals from these mares, when they arrive. This, I think, is a very healthful thing, as the more persons there are who become informed about something beside the betting angle of racing, the better it will be for the perpetuation of

of the sport. As the weather was so good all the
foals were out running for a sunning in the dryer
of the small paddocks. The little ones are becoming used to one another.

MARCH 30. Spent a few hours today with a
neighbor who lost the dam of a three-week-old
foal last night. As no foster mother was to be
found something had to be done pronto, so I ad-
vised treating the little colt as I did one a couple
of years ago. We got a bag of regular dried
milk and mixed it with warmed water and sugar
and fed him every two hours from a pan. The
proportions I used were a cup of dried milk, a
tablespoon of sugar and about two quarts of
water. The milk is stirred in like flour and the
sugar added to all. The advantage over fresh
cow's milk is that it is not necessary to keep
milk on hand; it is readily mixed and the unused
portion can be thrown out. My neighbor's foal
was drinking a little this evening, sucking on
my finger as I held it in the bowl. As he had a
taste for oats he will get some oatmeal also.

MARCH 31. All the mares and foals were out
again today, longer than ever before. Trials and
breeding go on apace. There are but four dry
mares yet to be bred, but it's a sure bet that
not all that have been bred are in foal. Vigilance
regarding the trials will not be relaxed until mid-
June with tests thrice weekly. The stallions are
working in fine fashion and the regular examinations show them to be as fertile as one would
wish. The long hair of winter is fast leaving all
of the mares and yearlings. These latter seem
to be growing right up in the air now. They are
not intended for the yearling sales and are being allowed to grow in the open and to rough it
as much as they can.

APRIL 1. All Fool's Day. Started off right by
getting badly fooled on a mare I had thought to
be in foal. She had been out of season for over
a month. She is back all right, and will be bred
again in a couple of days. We like to let the

mares get well in heat before we breed them. Was over to see the orphan on the neighboring farm today for a few minutes. He now has a sheep as a companion and the two are great friends already. The foal seems to thrive and the companionship will do him good. A dull overcast day, but the foals were able to get a couple hours out of doors. Those with the kinks of birth in their legs are already showing the beneficial effects of exercise and sunshine and are straightening up nicely.

APRIL 2. The busiest season of our year on the farms is now in full swing. Already we have bred 26 mares here and have sent several away. Yet one more filly arrived, quite unexpectedly this morning. The mare was still at the upper farm and was scheduled for moving down to the home farm along with three others which were to be moved today. It will not be necessary, in her case. The watchman up there found her nursing her foal, the foaling having been completed without aid or hindrance between his hourly trips around the barns.

APRIL 3. Increasing unrest on the part of an old mare who had looked like foaling for some days made it plain that her time was close when I turned in last night. It was close on midnight when the watchman gave the call and I rushed out to find the mare just ready to start operations. The fore legs, which were then protruding, showed that we had an exceptionally large customer to deal with, and so it proved, for the colt is the largest, by far, of the year's crop. The mare had a hard time and so did the watchman and I. To enable the watchman to pull better we tied a shank around each of the fore feet and slipped the rope around his back, thus giving a better opportunity to use his weight. I was busy manipulating the foal close up to the mare and lubricating things a little with olive oil. The hips gave us the most trouble and when they were out stimulants were indicated for the exhausted mare—she is one which is always a hard case at foaling time—as well as for us. Having about one good drink in the whiskey bottle, and plenty of strychnine in the medicine chest, it seemed wisest that the mare should have a couple of grains of the strychnine hypodermically, while I had the Scotch orally. Both of us were benefited by the treatment. The mare was up and cleansed after an hour or so of resting, and after the foal nursed I was glad to return to the house and bed.

APRIL 4. One of the fillies up at the upper farm was noticed to be lame this morning and on investigation was found to have run a thick splinter of wood into her foot, just inside the wall of the hoof. The splinter was drawn out and the foot poulticed with flax seed and the filly received a dose of tetanus antitoxin and seems to be fairly comfortable now. With over 100 head of horses around one gets these little accidents quite frequently.

APRIL 5. As the race track had been unfit yesterday, the 2-year-olds were all breezed up at the stable this morning. Sunday gave the stud men an opportunity to see their products working and they all collected to watch proceedings. All of the horses breezed along in nice shape and their trainer professed himself well satisfied with their progress. In just a few days they will leave the farm for the more serious business of earning their living in the real strife of the race course. Some may some day earn the right to return as breeding stock. The yearling filly seems to be coming along in fine shape and is hardly at all sore.

APRIL 6. Sunday's regular foal arrived last night at 9:30, another filly to be sure, but a really nice one. This was followed by the advent of yet one more of the same at 5:30 this morning. Today's filly is a big, straight-legged thing and both of the foals are progressing as they should. It is noticeable that these foals which are coming along just now are not as a rule as long behind time as the earlier arrivals nor is there much impaction of the lower bowels on arrival. We have had little trouble with this; so far not an enema has been found necessary. Took a semen sample from the premier stallion this morning and tested it for longevity. The semen was kept at a regular temperature for five hours and at the end was in very lively condition—the little chaps were vigourously swimming around. A short lived sample is not apt to get many mares in foal.

APRIL 7. Last night's foal was a colt for a change—Box score: colts 5, fillies 11; 16 down, 12 to go. There is still a chance for the colts to win but the odds seem to be against them. Eight of the younger foals had halters put on today and got a brief lesson in handling in the stalls. The shank was run through a ring in the stall wall and the foals got a good pull at it. All had their feet picked up and handled a little. The oldest foal had his feet trimmed, the smith using a small bladed, sharp knife. The yearling whose foot was injured is mending famously. The foot is still kept well covered to prevent the intrusion of dirt of any kind. One of the latest mares to foal has quite a little discharge, and has apparently torn herself. We have been irrigating her vagina and uterus with a boric acid solution.

APRIL 9. It looks as though some of the mares are getting stopped. Everything was tried this morning and the results were completely negative everywhere. I hope this is a good sign. Went up to the training quarters at noon to watch the string of 2-year-olds loaded into the vans for shipment to the race track where they will get their first taste of the real stuff of their lives. It was pleasant to watch close on a score of them go up into the vans without a bit of trouble anywhere. Not one had to be twitched or bothered at all. They were allowed ample time to walk in after a good look around. All had new white bandages on all four legs to safeguard them against injury. It is very important that nothing go amiss with the youngsters when first loaded, for they never forget. Another filly arrived while I was having supper. It is a neat thing and was nursing lustily thirty minutes after seeing the light of day. Twelve fillies to five colts now.

APRIL 10. On one of my frequent looks around the mares and foals this afternoon, I noted one little chap who was definitely dopey in appearance. The mare's bag was fuller than it should have been, which is a sure indication of an ill foal, so we milked her dry. The foal, which is just nine days old, is suffering from the regular attack of diarrhoea which comes along at that time. With him it seems very severe but he will doubtless be brighter in the morning. Spent the evening reading an extremely good booklet, *Notes on Horse Breeding*, compiled by the Remount Branch of the Quartermaster Corps. This supplies all manner of useful data pertinent to all phases of breeding and will be found invaluable to the breeder.

APRIL 11. A pretty nice colt arrived last night, making the score now just 2 to 1 for the weaker sex. The foal which was not nursing is fine this morning. We kept the dam dried out all last night. The mare's bag never fails to show the foal's health.

APRIL 12. Last night's foal was a filly, and by a winner of the Derby and Preakness at that. So it goes,—if one wants a colt one gets a filly, and vice versa. So much water standing everywhere that we decided not to turn out. If last winter was the coldest for aeons this spring must be the wettest. The usual Sunday influx of visitors was on hand to see the foals and one likes to see so much interest in the breeding and farm side of the business. All of the mares and foals are doing splendidly but they would be the better for more outdoor exercise.

APRIL 13 and 14. The past two and a half days have been spent in bed, with what these medicos term tonsilitis. It is awful for an outdoor man to have to stay in during the spring, but today I have been able to get some consolation out of reading every kind of horse magazine. Had the bed moved so that I could watch the stud activities from my window to some small extent, but it was a poor substitute for being out with the mares myself. Today's mail brought a letter from a gentleman who upbraided me lightly for regretting the number of our fillies, citing a case where his neighbor had 12 foals, all fillies but one. My friend is one who fortunately appreciates the value of the fillies and I expect to see some great horses emanate from his stud in time to come.

APRIL 15. Out and around once more today and picking up the strings dropped last week. Find the foals all doing very well and one notices sharply their growth in a short time when one is not constantly watching them. Shipped away another mare and foal this morning by van, as well as one yesterday. They will both be bred and left away until the end of the season. The one that went away yesterday was in season when she left but would not take the horse on arrival, probably due to the long van trip. She will be well tried again today after having had plenty of time to settle down. In spite of the tremendous amount of rain this spring the grass and the trees are greening up in fine shape. If we can just get a few good sunny, warm days the barren mares can all go out for the season soon.

APRIL 16. Another of those chestnut fillies came last night. They are endless. Today we moved the steers back to their old quarters in the corral where the winter's manure has been hauled. In the daytime they run out on the young rye in the small paddock and at night they go to the corral. The rye is getting dry now and today five of the mares in foal are pasturing on it. Tomorrow we will put the other four on the rye and these five will go back into one of the smaller grass paddocks.

APRIL 17. It is very cold today, and the foals were only out for a short time, the youngest ones not at all. This morning the fifteenth filly, another chestnut, appeared. Score, 15 to 6 in favor of the fillies, seven more to go. The farm crew is busy hauling manure all over the farm. Two men are going through the fields of rye and wheat, sowing the mixture of grass seed which will make them into pastures in time to come. They are using a goodly portion of lespedeza seed in their mixture, as this grass has been proved invaluable to us here.

APRIL 18. Took a day off to see the 3-year-olds run in the Chesapeake Stakes. Was well pleased with the showing of Grand Slam, which will improve a great deal off this race, unless I miss my guess. *Delphinium ran a corker to lead around and almost lasted to win. Found another of these young female horses—I'm sick of writing fillies—when I arrived home. A big slashing bay, this one, but no trouble to her dam.

APRIL 19. This morning I was strolling around, and looked the mares over en route to see the steers. My walk took me about 20 minutes, and on return I noticed that only six, instead of seven, mares were visible. The other had laid down and was going about the business of foaling while the rest of the mares stood in an uninterested circle around her. The foal, a bay colt —it would be from a visiting mare—was wrapped in a blanket, put in a hand cart and was trundled off to the stable with the mare following. In short order the youngster was up nursing. Spent most of the day showing off the place to a visiting ex-editor, and was glad to note that he appeared well satisfied with his inspection. Tonight—it is about morning as I write—we have had another colt, one from a 4-year-old maiden mare. The foal is a huge one and is doing well, but at the price of a worn-out mother. The mare had a very hard trip and at one time it appeared as though we should lose both. A strong constitution and good health prevailed.

APRIL 20. Another filly, a fine big one with no trouble anywhere, arrived this morning. The maiden who foaled last night is very sore and badly swollen today. She will need time and irrigations. Yesterday's foal, from the visiting mare, has had quite a lot of bowel trouble and we have had to give him an enema, two in fact. We gave him two ounces of glycerine, two tablespoonsful of peroxide of hydrogen in two quarts of warm soapy water. This was given in two doses, several hours apart. The second enema had the desired effect and the much relieved foal is nursing and resting happily.

APRIL 21. Today we have turned out the barren mares which for various reasons have been kept at the upper farm. They have joined those from the Madden shed and there are now about 18 head, maidens, visitors, barren mares and ponies which are running over 120 acres of good grass. The trials will be conducted now from the upper farm, instead of from here. The mares and foals with one exception were out all day today, for the first time for the most of them this spring. The four mares yet to foal are running on the rye paddock and it will be a welcome day when the last of them foals. The inevitable result of a few warm days was noted this morning when trying the barren mares. There were several in heat, showing that it never pays to be too sure of any of them.

APRIL 22. We have had a pretty sick foal here today. One of those which arrived during the week-end has had diarrhoea, apparently caused by the dam's having some fever from a slight infection which we have cleared up with antiseptic douches. The foal has not been nursing as he should and he has had to have a couple of whiskey toddies as well as two enemas of warm salt and water. He has had three doses of the mixture used for such cases and appears better.

APRIL 23. Tried all the barren mares this morning. Two were found in season so were

sent, one down to the home farm and one away,
for breeding. Hauled sand afresh today into the
stallion paddocks for sand beds for them to roll
on. The horses like this and it helps keep their
hair in condition. This afternoon we have had
mules chain-harrowing the paddocks at the home
farm. The sick foal is doing splendidly today,
nursing well and getting stronger. Two more
visiting mares came in today. One was covered
and returned, while the owner of the other elect-
ed to leave her for a month for trials.

APRIL 24. Rode up to the training stable today;
it is a dreary spot just now. The yearling colts
are all doing well and are out in the paddocks
all day. The men are tearing out a few rotten
pawing boards, around the outer edge of the
stalls. These are being replaced with new boards,
and the centers of the stalls are being dug up and
fresh clay and lime, well mixed, will be put in
and rammed hard. The stalls are being creosoted five feet up, and the higher walls and ceil-
ings are whitewashed with the spraying machine.
When all is dry and the stalls bedded the 17 yearling fillies will join the seven yearling colts up
there for the summer. It will be August before
they will be broken.

APRIL 25. Everything being shipshape on the
farm this morning, after the breeding and trials
were taken care of I took the family to see the
greatest cross-country race of America, the Maryland Hunt Cup. It was a wonderful sight to look
up from the paddock in the valley and to see
some 20,000 people massed on a hillside which
affords a natural grandstand from which every
step of the four-mile race can be seen.

APRIL 26. Sunday again, and somewhat warmer. The mares and foals out all day today. Took
a ride this morning, inspecting the fields and the
grass, as well as the mares scattered far and
wide. The grass is slowly coming but it is at least
two weeks behind. As we were at lunch a huge
black cloud drove across the western sky and

torrents of rain fell. Result, lunch spoiled, while we hustled back and forth between the stables and paddocks, taking up the mares and foals.

APRIL 27. Filly number 18 arrived at 2 a. m. A nice one and in good order. Only three more now. The farm crew is busy ploughing the land that is intended for corn. I rode through one old grass field that is on that part of the farm used by the dairy and saw them turning up about the only old grass we have on the place. The tractors are set deep and are doing a good job. The fields at the home farm that are in wheat and rye are looking splendid.

APRIL 28. A nice warm day with the mares and foals enjoying it to the limit. All talk hereabouts is of the Derby just now. Opinions are very varied but I stick to my October choice, of Mr. Woodward's Granville. I think he's cut out for a smasher. They all say Brevity, but these cinches often come unstuck.

APRIL 29. Trials of the mares keep on every other day. Today's was encouraging, for few of the more than 50 mares tried showed any interest in the stallions. The mail brought me a letter from far off Balboa, down by the Canal. I am asked by the writer about the chances of a keen young lad whose only love is the horse, getting a start on a stud-farm, and whether or not I think this a good place for him to start. Emphatically, I do. It is a good thing, to my mind, for any lad to get started at the beginning of all horses' lives, the farms. If a boy finds that the farm, rather than the race course, is his natural bent, then there is plenty of opportunity for him to get advancement. The arduous work, 24-hour duty at times, and the fact that a lad must love his job above all else, tend to keep the present day boys from sticking. It is a long grind, but the satisfaction coming from the production of a real horse makes it well worth while.

APRIL 30. On all hands one sees friends leaving for the focal spot of national attention, Louisville. We who are busy on the farms find it impossible to get away at this time. The race would suit us better in June, after our heavy responsibilities are over for awhile. All our lawns have been mowed around the stables this morning and it is a great improvement. The bare spots have had grass seed sown on them.

MAY 1. Today we moved the 18 yearlings fillies up to the training stable, in the three-horse van. Though it is only a three-mile run, the education in the van is useful to the youngsters. We took all the needed time and there was no hurry and no trouble. This afternoon we have moved 12 of the mares and foals to the upper farm. The home paddocks have had hard grazing, if one could call it that, all winter and spring, and now they will get a month's rest.

MAY 2. Derby Day. Today I have spent an interesting, though arduous, day, acting as judge in a horse show devoted entirely to kids under 21. It is a treat to watch the interest and keenness of these youngsters, and anyone who thinks that my colleague and I did not have a task, had better try placing 42 Thoroughbred hacks, all in one class. A mere 71 hunters came out in another class and we were constantly at it from 10 o'clock to 6:30 p. m.

MAY 3. It is very quiet in the stud yard today, all but a few mares and foals being at the upper farm. One has ample time to study the papers and consider the aftermath of the Derby. As I expected, and so wrote, the "Widener jinx" beat Brevity. One cannot help comparing the riding in our classic races here with the riding in these events over the water. Why the boys cannot learn to "run a straight course" I do not know. It's mighty hard on an owner, as well as on the trainer and the breeder of a horse like Brevity or Granville, to have years of effort spoiled by a pig-headed punk.

MAY 4. The peace of Sunday night was rudely shattered last night by the arrival of filly number 19. And what a game lass she is. In over a score of years watching mares foal I have never had a case like last night's. I had had a hunch for a week that there was trouble impending with this mare and was not at all surprised when only the off fore foot was presented, followed by a whacking big head. Manual investigation showed the other foot to be turned under the brisket with the leg doubled forward at the knee. In spite of efforts it was impossible to get the foal back so as to pull up the leg into the proper position, and the foal was as lively as a cricket all the time, some 45 minutes, that I was trying to get her out. As a last resort I determined to risk losing the foal to save the mare, so tied one rope around the foal's neck and one around the fetlock of the leg that was out, both ropes being tied to a stout ringbolt on the stall wall. With plenty of olive oil poured in for a lubricant, we pushed the mare away from the wall and out came the filly. She was quickly loosened and turned on her back and fore legs manipulated back and forth while she was well rubbed with straw at the same time. In short order she was as right as a trivet and in 20 minutes was up. The mare stayed up while the stall was cleaned and ate a mash and enjoyed a good warm toddy. She, too, is doing well.

MAY 5. Just one more mare to foal. Filly number 20 arrived without untoward incident about 1:00 a. m. this morning, not a bad little thing at all. The yellow mustard weed is appearing in the fields, and today we are pulling them up by the roots. The chain-harrowing is going along fast now, for we have a tractor hitched to the harrow. The implement is doing a great amount of good, filling the holes made by horses' feet in the bad weather, and spreading the droppings.

MAY 6. Our Man o' War filly had a bit of bad luck today. Something running in the field with her must have jumped on her from behind, just skinning the outer edge of the tendon of the near hind leg. She is bandaged up like an oldster to-night, with a wet pack under the bandage. A smart little thing, she lies down with no one holding her, and allows her leg to be bandaged and dressed. Nor has she attempted to bite off the bandage or bother it at all, though it must be irksome to have it on her leg. She should be well again in a couple of weeks.

MAY 7. This has been a busy day here. The very wet early spring has caused more than the usual supply of wood-ticks to be on hand and this morning we had all the barren mares in for inspection and any indicated treatment. We found several of the mares had sores on the mane and tail, at the roots of the hairs. These we treated with a useful mixture to have around the farm for these regular spring troubles. The mix-ture, which anyone can make up, consists of Ly-sol, 2 ounces; tincture of iodine, 2 ounces; pow-dered sulphur, 1½ ounces; cottonseed oil enough to make up a quart of the mixture. This can be dabbed on with a wad of absorbent cotton.

MAY 8. The filly which arrived a couple of days ago has a rather weak off hind ankle which is much inclined to knuckle over. To overcome this trouble we have put a brace on her and she goes much better. The brace is made by building up the thickness of the pastern to the thickness of the ankle with cotton and then a strip of thick leather is cut to the required length and width. The leather is put over the ankle and fetlock while soaking wet and sheet cotton and a tight bandage are rolled over all. The drying leather forms a cast for the ankle. The thin layer of cotton under the leather protects the leg. The whole is removed three or four times during the day and night and is left off for fifteen minutes or so.

MAY 9. The foaling season at the Sleepy Hol-low Stud is over for 1936, thank goodness. The last arrival, a strongly made, rugged colt, showed up at 2:00 a. m. this morning, his coming being without .incident. The score of the home owned mares is 20 fillies, eight colts, one mare slipped twins. All the foals are doing well today. The filly with the brace on her ankle and fetlock is much improved therefrom and we shall leave the bandage off in a couple of days.

MAY 11. The mares seem to be getting settled fairly well. Only three out of fifty-odd in season, two of them of that type of barren mare which is the studmaster's despair all season long. The mares are doing well out on the grass now, though all the grass fields need the rain. The men have been busy giving the stables a good cob-webbing all 'round and taking the windows out so that the maximum of air circulation can be had in hot weather. We are keeping the stallions in now in the hot part of the day and turning them out all night; they are likely to run too much flesh off galloping in the heat of the day.

MAY 12. Drove some 250 miles today inspecting some of the mares and foals we have sent to various farms for the covering season. Found all the foals thriving and grown in good shape. It appears as though everyone is having his troubles getting the mares in foal during this changeable season. The need of rain in this area is universal; everywhere I drove I heard complaints. The superabundance of filly foals seems to be coming in for its usual amount of bewailing too.

MAY 13. It is shoeing time again today and this time the foals are coming in for some attention. Those which are over six weeks or so old usually are ready for trimming. They usually struggle around a good deal at first but if a good man has their heads and another man the tails, holding the foal against the wall thus, there is no trouble controlling them. The mares and foals all had their manes and tails examined for ticks, etc., at the time they were in. It looks as if they will be able to get out nights pretty soon. All the little ones are on the mend now. The brace has been left off the filly's ankle entirely and it is sound as a bell.

MAY 14. The work among the animals of the stud is slackening up to some extent. There are fewer barren mares, and nursing mares, too, coming in season and the trials show that we are getting somewhere with the breeding program. The broken nights and suspense of waiting is over for the year and the weather is becoming such that the majority of the stock will soon be outdoors. We have not turned out the mares and foals all night as yet, which is unusual this late. Last night we had a grand refreshing rain, there being two heavy storms which did us a world of good.

MAY 15. Today I have been watching the farm crew preparing the land for corn and I noted the lime they were spreading. This will do a lot of good. The farm should grow a lot of corn and cow peas if all is well, this year. The wheat and rye look very good, indeed, but the prospects for a long crop of hay are poor in our part of the country just now. Since the rains of the other night it is quite noticeable how the grass has sprung up.

MAY 16. Preakness Day. Away bright and early to see the 3-year-olds contest the historic Preakness, and a great day we all had. I thought the colts a fine looking lot and had the satisfaction of picking the winner, which only just beat Granville, my choice before I looked the horses over in the paddock. It was an awful job getting around in the jam but still I had a chance to learn from Mr. Woodward that his connections were very much enthused over Omaha's win in England. Curiously enough there seems to be quite a strong impression in many quarters that the chestnut colt won over a dirt track at Kempton. Such is not at all the case.

MAY 17. Spent most of the morning strolling around the paddocks with a keen young friend whose comment on the stock was entertaining indeed. Found all doing well and flourishing and the grass much improved since last I went through it. The harrowing is in some measure responsible for this, I think.

MAY 18. We have had a busy Monday today; it always seems that way. This morning we opened up a new trough at ground level for the artesian well in the large fields where the barren mares now are. This is a cement trough at ground level, into which the water continuously flows. There is an overflow pipe at the end. We have these troughs cleaned out about three times weekly when the fields are in use. Only one mare was in season when all got their regular trials this morning. This evening we have had three thunderstorms and warm rain.

MAY 19. It has been quite cool again today after the rain, more of which arrived this morning. We had all the foals' feet looked over this afternoon. Several did not need any attention but a good many of those which were too young for it last time needed trimming up a bit. Had a good ride this morning all over the farm. We have hung small wicket gates with convenient hooks in the fences between the fields, so that one never needs to go on the roads to get from place to place anymore.

MAY 20. Thirty foals all doing well was too good to last for very long and this morning tragedy came. While playing about in the fields one of the filly foals was apparently kicked squarely on the right knee and is very sore. My examination led me to believe that there was at least one bone broken in the knee and when the veterinarian got here he doubled my idea and found two small ones fractured. There is little we can do for the little thing. She will never race, that's sure. We will save her for breeding in time to come, I hope, for she is from regal lineage and we held high hopes for her. The near fore leg is well done up in cotton and

bandages, as is the off hind. This is to strengthen
the joints of these members so that they will
carry the additional load put upon them by the
useless leg.

MAY 21. Rather cold nights, and frequently
quite damp ones, are keeping the foals still
indoors at nights. We are later turning them out
than I remember for some years. It is better,
I think, to run no risks with the little ones and
to leave them in than to have them down with
sickness. Had a good long ride over the place
here and the surrounding territory today. The
crops are looking in fine shape except for the
hay. The winter grains are good and we are
going to have a good lot of straw for our use
next winter. It is a good thing that we will have
a hundred-odd acres of soy beans and cow peas
to add to the hay crop. We use these extensively;
the majority of the mares are fed nothing else
during the late fall and they go into winter in
fine bloom. This year we should have enough to
see the mares in the Madden shed through the
bad weather.

MAY 22. Today we have had a visit from some
of the veterinary staff of our state college, who
were anxious to get blood samples from some of
the mares for testing on virgin rats to determine whether the mares are pregnant or not.
Always willing to help out in anything of this
sort, we furnished 10 mares, some nursing, some
barren, some maidens and one that slipped twins.
The 15 or so c. c. of blood taken from the jugular
vein is made into a serum which is shot into the
rats and in a few days the latter are destroyed.
Certain changed conditions indicate conclusively
whether or not the mare is in foal. This method
is good, I think, where there are no available
practitioners who can determine pregnancy early
on in its course.

MAY 23. We have had the crippled foal out
for awhile this morning; she gets along surpris-
ingly well on her three good legs. These are

well bandaged still to strengthen them. It's going to be a long pull for her and there may be a stiff knee at the end of it. We shall see, however, how it goes. Have been sitting out in the shade on the lawn just now, listening to the broadcasting of the running of the Withers. Poor old Brevity—he must be jinxed in some way.

MAY 24. It is quite warm here today, really a seasonable day. The mares and foals are lazing out in the fields, standing around in bunches switching themselves lazily with their tails. I found the band of mares out in the Big Woods field, after a long search, deep in the woods where they have a cool glade over which the boughs of the trees arch like a cathedral roof. We have put a big salt block there for their convenience, for they will be spending considerable time loafing there from now on. All of the stock appeared to be thriving when leisurely inspected today. One or two mares seem to be putting too much feed into their own back, rather than on the foals. This is hard to correct. Supplementary rations are indicated for the foals when they all start spending the hot days indoors.

MAY 25. It has been plenty warm again today, though a nice breeze tempered the heat to some extent. We have started in about the last week of the breeding season, everything tried and only one in season of the whole lot today. We shipped one mare and foal home this morning.

MAY 26. Last night we turned the mares and their foals out after they had been brought in for their evening meal. It was a good warm night and all did well. Today we have had them in all day and this will be the regular order of things through the hot weather. There seem to be many advantages here to be gained by following this plan. The foals come in after their night in the open and lie down and rest, there are fewer flies to bother them, and if the mares do kick at a fly there is less chance of a foal being kicked indoors than when all are milling around in the open. The mares and their foals will get three feeds a day now, at 6, 11, and 4:30.

MAY 27. Hurried through with the morning inspection of horses and treatments of the few minor cripples to get back to the radio to listen to the running of the Derby, broadcast from Epsom. The all-conquering Blandfords did the trick once more when the Aga Khan's Mahmoud came from behind to win from Taj Akbar, with the entry from my native heath, the northern trained Thankerton, in third place.

MAY 28. After yesterday's heavy storm, when we had a 45-mile wind for a few minutes, as well as a good heavy rainfall, we had the mares and foals in for the night. Rode all over the farm this morning and observed the regular trials of the mares, one being found to be in season of all the lot. The work of the stallions will soon be over now and they are not covering with any regularity now. This is the time of the year for frayed dispositions on the part of the sires. While the barren mares were up for observation they had their feet gone over by the blacksmith. Three were shod and a couple more trimmed. They are in very fine condition just now and it looks as though a good lot are in foal from all indications.

MAY 29. Plenty cold here this morning. The thermometer was down to 35. Watched the gardeners who brought the new power mower over here this morning. This implement is going to make our lawn cutting—a really arduous job when its hot—a lot easier to handle. We have about four acres of lawn about the stud and it takes some mowing by hand. The men have been cleaning up around the place, raking the yard, trimming edges of the lawns and so on in preparation for the long week-end as tomorrow is a holiday.

MAY 30. Decoration Day. Nothing but essentials going on here today. One man only at each farm on duty. Had a long drive this morning to see a colt that I'm interested in get his final work before shipping to the Big Apple for racing. Roads crowded and driving rotten. On returning home found word had come from the college people that of the 11 mares whose blood was sampled all are apparently in foal except one, not one of our own at that. This mare has not been bred or in season since March 11 and now we will have to try to bring her in season and get her bred, as her owner is more interested in getting a foal than bothering about it being a late one. This test shows how mares will fool one occasionally.

MAY 31. We seem to be all balled up with yesterday and today both rest days. Two loafing days get tiresome. Took one of the men with me for a drive around the place, looking over everything as we went around. Found the horses all doing well and our black steers particularly so. Nothing else much to do but read and plan out the return of our various mares from afar. Mares and foals and yearlings are all in days now, out nights, which latter are still cool enough for a blanket.

JUNE 1. A busy Monday morning. Everything tried and two mares bred about three weeks ago in season. One was bred today, the other will be tomorrow. No need for using the horse twice a day now any more. He will be tailed off gradually into disuse in a week or ten days. Found to my satisfaction that the three visitors which had caused gray hairs all season are apparently settled as they are in their fifth week now and look good. They are housing the first cutting of alfalfa up at the dairy this afternoon. It is nice and green but too fibrous for our use. We will have some from a later cutting.

JUNE 2. Today we have started shipping home the mares which have been visiting outside stal-

lions. The van just got in from a 14-hour trip,
as I write, with one mare whose foal looks very
good after his visit. I hope the mare is in foal
but it's doubtful for she proved how little one
can be certain of this by coming in season last
Saturday after going seven weeks. The men who
made the trip report that the grass situation is
very serious in the country through which they
passed.

JUNE 3. Another mare arrived to one of our
stallions this morning. Her owner is an optimis-
tic soul but the mare will be useful to us by
reason of the horse in question doing quite a bit
of trying mares without many to breed. The
manager of our dairy came over for a visit this
morning with the result that we have about 20
head of dry Jersey cows and heifers divided
among four of the smaller paddocks. These cattle will help eat off the coarser long grass which
the horses do not care about.

JUNE 4. We found two more mares in season
this morning and immediately sent one away
for service again; the other we bred here. Both
had passed to their sixth week. Spent a couple of
hours this evening, when it was cool, looking over
the yearlings at the training stable. They seem
to be growing well. One notes the development
of physical characteristics and a growing away
from the baby form. It is very quiet up there
now with nothing but the "young entry" on
hand. Things will liven up plenty in August
when breaking commences.

JUNE 5. A busy day today. Everything gone
over, a couple of foals trimmed and another
mare and foal back from breeding away. More
haste, less speed is a word that was brought
home to me today when ill-advisedly hustling the
old Major over one of the lately graveled roads.
Result: one horse stood on his head—he picked
up a large round gravel between his calks on
the near fore and went over a bit rapidly—and

one rider with a stiff shoulder and a thumb that doesn't like a typewriter.

JUNE 6. What a glorious day. Could fill this week's space with an account of the Belmont. And that old dark nose was on the outside and just in front at the right moment today. The look of satisfaction on the Woodward visage was worth the trip up alone. I've got to apologize to Granville for doubting his stamina after the Preakness, though. I didn't know he had his sire's habit of loafing when in front, then, and he fooled me badly. Granville clinched his title, at least until Max Hirsch, a sad looker-on today, can try Bold Venture again.

JUNE 7. Got home in the cool of the evening and found one of the boys awaiting me to "go round" the horses with me. This we did, finishing before dark came upon us, and it was good to find all in good order with the only cloud on the horizon being the lack of rain, Irish though that sounds. Anyway the trip was well worth while and I shall not be at all surprised if I looked at next year's Belmont winner when appraising the two fine lots of 2-year-olds performing yesterday. So it's back to work again, the better for the break.

JUNE 8. Busy today picking up the threads again. Everything tried and but one mare in season, she having refused the horse since April 20. We will cover her once more and wish for luck, even though it is a bit late. Up near the training quarters they are starting the harvesting of the grain. The field of rye that they are cutting is about an average crop with some fine long straw. They are using a new self-binder which cuts a swath of 10 feet and is drawn by a rubber-tired tractor. I watched one of the men blowing up a tire on the tractor, and, though only 10 pounds pressure is needed, the size of the tire gave him enough to do. Showers appear to be in the offing, and goodness knows they're needed.

JUNE 9. This morning we moved half a dozen steers from the now short pastured paddocks by the training stable, taking them in the van to the big pastures of the upper farm. We drove the van into the field and no more was an attempt made to lower the chute than out the whole lot came, one after another, just like sheep. The barren mares in this field are looking very well. We had seven of them in this afternoon for various attentions at the hands of the blacksmith. The ground is getting so hard now that with standing around switching at flies, the mares feet break up worse than at any other time. There has been little natural moisture to keep them soft so far this summer. The little filly that broke her knee is hobbling around much better than she has been. Apparently that knee is not going to be permanently stiff.

June 10. The fields of grain are fast changing from a deep green to the golden hue of ripeness and the new binder is steadily eating its way through the standing crop. Soon they will be thrashing and we will be getting some good new straw. A load came in today from the dealer's and rotten short stuff it was. Good straw is at a premium just now and we still use a good deal, as there are about 75 stalls in regular use during the daytime. At night almost all are empty. It has been pleasantly cool today, and tonight the horses are all grazing contentedly. I have just come in from checking over the water troughs in the small paddocks. As the ground is so dry we bail out quite a little water from the troughs each evening to make it muddy around them. This helps to keep the mares' feet from getting too dry.

JUNE 11. We can write finis to the breeding season of 1936 today. All the mares were tried this morning for the last time. Results all negative. There are still half a dozen mares to come home. About an equal number of visitors are still here, though they lessen daily. The latter portion of the season has not been so bad but the first half was mighty tough on stallions and studmasters too. It's all to be expected, though, when ones tries to hasten nature's processes and tries to make winter into a breeding season. Sap rises in the spring—but not at all sooner. Have been loafing this evening and reading the very fine souvenir of Keeneland that Brownie Leach and J. A. Estes got up. Anyone interested in the traditions of racing in Kentucky should send and get a copy; its full of tales of the days of yore.

JUNE 12. We had three welcome hours of rain last night and the van crew, getting home from a 375-mile run with a mare and foal, reported the rain general over a large area. This morning we can see benefits from the rain already, even if it did stop the haying, which commenced yesterday. They are getting in the mixed clover and timothy hay up by the training quarters.

JUNE 13. A cool pleasant sort of day with a good breeze. After the morning's work was over Mrs. N. V., the kids, and I went to a real pony show not far from here and saw some real fine Shetlands as well as all sorts and shapes of others. It was a treat to see four-in-hands, tandems, pairs, and so on again. The driving classes are almost a thing of the past at most shows. Stopped by the stud farm of a friend on the way back and saw some very fine foals by a son of dead *Light Brigade which looks like carrying on in his sire's place. A good Fair Play scion and a Futurity winner of the fast Domino breed make up a well balanced trio of sires.

JUNE 14. A memorable day in more ways than one. To start with it rained off and on all day. Lightly, it is true, but rain nevertheless. Secondly the day was most noteworthy in that we spent the majority of it entertaining the editor of this journal and his wife who were paying us a long awaited visit. The farm, the local sights, and the horses and gardens came in for full inspection. We found our farm manager very pleased with himself as he showed us the reports of the state officials who had inspected his wheat crops. The reports certified one field of 65 acres for sale for seed as it had a very high standard of freedom from weeds, etc. All the grain fields showed up very well in the reports. Our head stallion was discovered to have struck himself this morning but he was not lame, merely a little filled. A rubbing with Absorbine and a bandage will fix him up in short order.

JUNE 15. The stallion's ankle is normal again. The whole horse population of the farm was closely inspected this morning when one of the partners of the British Bloodstock Agency called upon us. The van brought home the last of the mares from away this morning and it will now get a coat of paint and will be put by for the summer. The mare in question just arrived in time for inspection, and, like the majority, she passed with honors. Our foreign guest and I had an interesting discussion on the question of breeding from mares which had been stimulated while racing and he agreed with me that it took three or four stud seasons to correct the damage done to the genital organs by the "hop".

JUNE 16. Spent the morning going over the stock once more with our visiting expert and many were the interesting yarns he had to tell of horses in all climes. Had all the mares' and foals' feet attended to that have just gotten home. Most of the foals needed trimming a bit, but the majoriy of the mares were in good shape.

JUNE 17. The wheat harvest started this morning with the tractor-hauled binder sweeping through the fine crop in fast time. Found one mare in season this morning; she had been away but we were doubtful about her being in foal, as she "broke" at nine weeks. It's too late to do anything for her now, so she will go barren and will be covered early next season. One of the foals has had a filled ankle, from a kick upon it. The enlargement looked like staying with her, and we have started painting it with a light iodine paint this evening, as this will tighten it up and reduce the permanent enlargement.

JUNE 18. Gold Cup Day at far away Ascot, where four days of racing programs hold nothing but stakes, and good ones too. We lost little time hurrying through the morning inspections to get back to the radio to hear what would happen. Just as we were about set, with the field at the post, there came a call from the upper farm that brooked no delay. Result, no hearing of the broadcast and frantic phoning, only to learn that after we had touted him as a sure thing for the Cup for a year, Omaha had been beaten a short head. No disgrace there, though, for it was Quashed that beat him, a fine stayer if ever there was one, and another "bar-sinister half-bred," an Irish one this time. One's sympathies go out to that gallant American gentleman, William Woodward tonight. The mail today included a letter from a stud owner in Jamaica, B. W. I., who brought up a number of questions which I shall have to answer at length. The gentleman felt encouraged to write inasmuch as I had noted receiving a letter from Balboa and I'm right glad he did. (So are some of the little Ventures, who like foreign stamps). Chief of his troubles is worms, so I am sending him a copy of the U. S. Government's latest very full bulletin on the subject.

JUNE 19. The younger generation of this farm being here for the summer months, we have been busy getting the saddle horses and ponies in condition for riding. Today we have been busy getting two of the ponies and one saddle horse ready for a show tomorrow. The old Major is going too, so tonight he has his pins done up in cotton and bandages to tighten up some of the old windpuffs, etc., which years of honest toil have put there. I have been using something entirely new in an electric vacuum horse-cleaning outfit and I must say that I found it an excellent innovation. There is no dust to be inhaled when this is used and the results on the horses' coats are fine.

JUNE 20. A blazing hot day for a horse show, particularly when said show was held in a shadeless infield of a deserted race track. We cannot kick, however, for the new pony won a couple of blues for little owner-rider, two more of the young entry won ribbons in a lead-in class and the old Major distinguished himself by placing third in an open saddle class, carrying his nigh a score of years like a 2-year-old. It was a pleasant day, despite blowing sand of the ring and the sunburn.

JUNE 21. Before it got too hot, we "went round" the horses and found all in and in good order. The foals are growing in the right way; they are not just fat but are developing their true shape to some extent as they grow upwards. The yearlings are coming along very well. The trainer has them in fit condition from the vigorous exercise they take in the very early mornings. One feels true condition on them when handling them; the flesh is firm and there is a bloom to it.

JUNE 22. The airplanes which have been flying about us all summer have intensified their activities very much the past few days. They habitually do this over the farm and this morning, before we took the mares and foals up, there were six planes circling and dipping around the place. We used not to like this but we have observed that the horses pay practically no attention and we have decided that the farm is a good place for the youngsters to get used to the planes. I believe they would hardly look up if a plane landed in their paddocks now.

JUNE 23. Very much cooler today, and a delightful change. The grain crop is fast being harvested, the standing grain disappearing and reappearing as shocks. Today we took blood samples from 21 mares which had passed 42 days since last service, and as time goes on we will test all of the mares and then check up again later. With forty-odd mares one can try the thing out properly. We took the supporting bandages from the legs of the crippled foal at the upper farm this morning. She gets along very well, without any trouble at all and the broken knee is not at all stiff. The filly that was cut down is much better. Five of the foals have developed hernia of different sizes but we will leave them alone entirely until they are well weaned. Lots of them disappear, so we always give them a chance to do it themselves.

JUNE 24. Late yesterday evening the clouds commenced banking up in the nor'east and it got much colder, with occasional light showers. Accordingly we kept up the mares and foals, and a good thing too, for we had welcome and heavy rainfall almost all night, and this morning it is still raining. Even though it has stopped the harvest temporarily, the rain will be a Godsend.

JUNE 25. Through the kindness of a friend I received today a card index of about a thousand stallions and in checking it over I noted a few missing. I'm going to ask the readers of the Diary to let me know of any changes of ownership of their sires, as I would like to keep this index up to date and available to anyone at any time. One of the younger mares, a good game winner, was very ill this morning with some sort of intestinal trouble and we had the best veterinary attention for her in short order. She got medicines of various kinds and took them all in good part. I thought she was going to die but her great heart would not let her, and with a horse that's more than half the battle. Tonight the mare seems to be resting better and to have an even chance for recovery.

JUNE 26. Up early and at the upper farm as soon as dressed. Found the mare still holding her own and I think a little better. She seems happier, if somewhat tired. Her foal has been nursing at her a bit, but chiefly she eats from the feed box. As it is hot we keep the mare sponged off lightly with alcohol and water. Tonight she is definitely better. The other mares and foals are doing very well, despite the almost brown color of the pastures.

JUNE 27. The sick mare seems to be slowly mending. She is game to the core and I think she is going along the right way. The foal seems not to be bothered by the somewhat diminished milk supply but is going strong on the water and feed. He goes right after the green feed we cut for the pair of them; it is soft and tastes good to them.

JUNE 28. I had a walk over some parts of the farm after "going 'round" the horses, all of which were doing nicely, the sick mare included. The corn has shot up since last week's rain and the large field of cow peas and soy beans are looking exceptionally well. If there should come a drouth one can always feed these latter as green feed. In the drouth of 1930 we fed cow peas all summer. Cut one day and hauled to the stock the next, they like them better than fresh cut.

JUNE 29. Our sick mare is very much better today and is fast getting herself back to normalcy. Her foal is evidently well pleased with the changes as we are. The blacksmith has been shoeing the saddle horses, which are now getting plenty of work in the cool of the early morning, this being the only decent time to ride in the hot weather. I noticed today that there were some worms showing up in a few of the foals' droppings and so we will very soon be giving them a dose apiece of the Frey's Vermifuge. This is not hard on them and they do not have to be drawn for it. It takes care of the worst of them until weaning time, when they will get the regular treatment.

JUNE 30. They are building a big shed, which is hereabouts termed a "barracks" up near the training stable, about mid-way of the farm. This is to house under a roof all the baled straw, hay, etc., which heretofore we have had to store outdoors when the barn lofts were filled up. I watched the yearlings eating their suppers and went down the line with the trainer as he inspected the feed boxes to see that all were well cleaned up. It looks as though there will be some handsome youngsters to send out next spring for racing.

JULY 1. I have just been watching the mares and foals being turned out here at the home farm. It is interesting to see. The first thing all the dams do is go to the new sand beds and take a roll, a few of the more intrepid of the foals imitating them. As soon as they are satisfied all seem to like a bit of speed trial and off they go. Today we had word from the Live Stock Sanitary Board about the 19 blood samples of in foal mares we sent over for examination last week. One was found to be barren, which was correct as manual examination showed this afternoon—one was doubtful and will be tested again in a couple of weeks, 16 were in foal and one other mare we cannot be sure about as the two rats that had been injected with her serum got away. However, there were found to be three, all positive, in another mare's cage where there should have been two, so it is likely they just went visiting.

JULY 2. Hot and sticky with high humidity. Last night we had a few small showers. This evening we have spent a few hours with a couple of rat terriers, a hose, and some sticks, trying to rid ourselves of some of the many rats that are always on hand. With the hose running cold water down the holes, the rodents soon pop out and then the dogs get their chance. If the dogs do not catch them the men, who are carefully posted, get them with the sticks. The colored lads enjoy the fun of the chase, all except one husky, who insists on getting on the highest point available to watch and encourage the others. He yells loudest of all at a kill. The little rat terriers are game as can be.

JULY 3. Several hours drive through a wet, dull morning brought me to a pleasant little country town in central Virginia, where, with a couple of colleagues, I have been judging an interesting and keenly contested horse show. The judging has been no easy task, as the classes have been well filled and the quality of the exhibits of a high calibre. The majority of the horses are hunters, and most of these are cleanbred or so close that it is often not easy to differentiate between them, as far as looks go. The hunters going over the outside course have to gallop along over a long, stiff hillside course and are well tried. As usual, the percentage on conformation is high, 50 to 60 per cent in some classes. The country hereabouts has been benefited by the recent rains but corn is not good, nor is hay.

JULY 4. Still at the judging job. Several classes today were for yearlings and 2-year-olds by Thoroughbred sires suitable to make hunters. Some were good ones but far too many were mediocre. The winner of the 2-year-old class is one of the biggest colts I have seen in years, about 16.2 and not an early foal. His dam claims *Light Brigade for sire and her son attests the claim. A good and heavy thundershower came along just as we finished judging the Championship, and we were saved a near drowning. The rain did interfere to some extent with the race, which attracted the ancient has-beens from the "leaky-roof" circuit. I noted with some surprise a horse by the name of Charley J. S. winning one of these scrambles and I recalled the day when he was running in good company about a decade ago. It's pitiful to see these once good 'uns fallen so low.

JULY 5. Spent the morning driving home and the most of a hot, sticky afternoon in going over the horses here. Found all well and doing as they should be. The ones which had been sick or crippled are doing splendidly and I was glad indeed to note that plenty of showers had fallen at home during my absence. The paddocks now have a pleasing green cast to them again, instead of the brownish look that they had for awhile.

JULY 6. A near tragedy occurred today. As we were leading in the mares and foals one of the latter broke loose from her handler and, frightened by the swinging shank, set sail away up the road with the man and the mare running after her as fast as they could. The filly ran half a mile or more and then slipped down, thus giving us time to catch her. Fortunately her troubles are superficial, but they might have been otherwise. She will be stiff for a few days, and, I hope, a little wiser. Have been showing off Sleepy Hollow Stud to my correspondent from Balboa, Canal Zone, today. The gentleman availed himself of an opportunity of seeing this farm while within reasonable reach of it, and we much enjoyed showing him the horses.

JULY 7. Hot and humid here today, but with a pleasant relief in the shape of a good breeze tonight. The filly that staged the act yesterday is pretty stiff today, but not as sore as I had expected her to be. We have boiled out her wounds with peroxide and are doctoring the bruised bone with hot water. Permanganate of potash solution keeps the wounds dry and icthyol ointment well rubbed in helps keep up the effects of the hot fomentations. These surface wounds are often uglier and harder to heal than a straight cut.

JULY 8. A good stiff breeze was welcomed today to temper the heat, the horses in their stalls have been sweating freely. They are out now and have had their rolls in the sand bed. Had a look this morning at a dozen or so yearlings that a prominent breeder is sending to Saratoga. They are well grown and carry plenty of flesh, considerably more than do our own, which are not being fitted for the sales ring.

JULY 9. This has been by long odds our hottest day so far this year. The horses in their stalls have sweltered all day long and it has been worse outside. We turned out early as there was a breeze coming up which the animals appreciated as much as we did. Had a call from a neighbor this morning who had a mare and foal, the former of which works. He was alarmed because he worked the mare yesterday and this morning one side of her bag is swollen and full of fever. I suggested milking her out frequently and massaging the udder with the milk, also fomenting the bag frequently with Epsom salts and hot water. Evidently the mare went too long yesterday without having the full bag relieved. As she is said to be a very heavy milker she should have been milked out every couple of hours, at least, while the foal was away from her.

JULY 10. The horses seem to be making the best of the heat (now at 104 degrees), but none of us are guilty of any unneccessary movement. We received from The Jockey Club this morning the certificates of registration of last year's foals, so tomorrow morning—it may be cooler then—I will check them over with the markings of the yearlings so that there will be no discrepancies.

JULY 11. As it is Saturday there has been nothing done this afternoon. I have been sitting in the shade in the cool end of one of the broodmare barns listening to the darkies discussing some of the horses we have had here in days gone by. They do not forget, but follow with interest the careers of their old charges after they are grown and are racing. They love to liken their favorites among the new foal crop with some of the old ones that have made good, though at times the resemblance seems faint to me.

JULY 12. Another very hot day. Looked over all the horses in the cool of the morning as soon as they came in and found all doing well. The minor cripples are getting along well with their various healing processes. It seems as though there must always be a few invalids of one sort or another with some hundred head of blooded stock alone. Have been bringing up to date the mare sheets in my BLOOD-HORSE *Stallion Register* this morning. I find it very handy to have them arranged alphabetically in the back of my book and have just got typed in the foaling dates of the 1936 foals, breeding dates for this year, and names of the 2-year-olds, as well as filling in the notation "winner" against quite a few of the names of the 2- and 3-year-olds listed under the mares.

JULY 13. Storms last night appreciably cooled the atmosphere. Taking advantage of the cooler weather and breeze, we had about 15 of the foals' feet trimmed, as well as a few of the mares fixed up at the same time. The foals are mostly past the "baby foot" stage and their feet are growing out past the ridge that marks the first growth of hoof. Tomorrow we will move about eight mares from the upper farm down here and transfer an equal number up there, for the change seems to do them good, even though it is but a few miles. The barren mares will be sent back to the quarters they occupied during the winter, and they will have the Madden shed to go into whenever they wish.

JULY 14. It was not so very hot this morning, so we moved the mares around. Tonight they are renewing old acquaintances and making new ones among their new paddock mates. The mares which have been separated for several months seem to look over the foals from their old friends with skeptical eyes, and there is much discussion of the grazing situation and so forth. The barren mares were all examined for loose shoes, etc., before being changed, and about half a dozen were shod or trimmed. They will all stay in their new quarters for a month or more before being changed again. We have ordered three dozen of the small bottles of Frey's Vermifuge, two ounces each, and we will give them to the foals tomorrow if they get here in time. There is syrup and oil of chenopodium in the stuff and the foals usually do not mind taking it with the syringe.

JULY 15. Hot and oppressive in the extreme today. So much so that we deferred the administration of the worm dope to the foals.

JULY 16. We gave the 29 foals their vermifuge this afternoon and one and all took it as though they liked it. The wormseed oil in the stuff will kill off a lot of ascarids.

JULY 17. Borrowed a set of harness and a good stout road cart from a friend to see how our old saddle horse, The Major, would act in the shafts. The old chap watched the fitting of the harness with a somewhat jaundiced eye but as he made no objections we put him in the shafts to see what would happen. Lo and behold, we have been unwittingly harboring a fine driving horse in our midst for long. The Major went sailing up the road in fine style and we had a pleasant drive around the farm before the heat drove us to cover.

JULY 18. Cooler today, but with unpleasant humidity. We have no cause to kick, however, for a letter from a breeder in the drought area of the Northwest brings distressing tidings of suffering among horse breeders up there. Many will sacrifice the work of years of assembling Thoroughbred and near-Thoroughbred broodmare bands, unless some of the Government's relief money is diverted to them.

JULY 19. Harnessed up The Major to the road cart before breakfast and, with the three kids in the bottom, set off on a tour of the fields and horses. Found all the barren mares—we hope that most of them are now in foal—down under the trees by the artesian well with its big trough of cool water that they love so well. All were in order, no loose shoes or cuts, so we drove on to the upper farm. Here the darkies got a kick out of our load in the cart. Saw the mares and foals come in. The foals are growing and the mares look well. We supplement the rations now, as the grass is very dry. Gus, foreman at this point, reported that worms had shown up in about two-thirds of the stalls after our treatment of three days ago.

JULY 20. This morning we had a long and heavy rain which will do untold good. The blacksmith has been busy again today fixing up the mares' feet and shoeing one of the stallions. He is constantly on the go, for, with the fields very dry, the mares stamp off a lot of shoes.

JULY 21. We took advantage of the let-up in the hot weather to send the van on a long trip after a 3-year-old filly which will join our broodmare band next spring. She arrived tonight and is a very nice feminine sort that looks like making a producer of the right sort. She had that look in her countenance that betokens a maternal disposition and is obviously a good "doer."

JULY 22. Our new acquisition came in for some attention today. As she is just out of training, we gave her a physic ball to clean her out thoroughly. Her teeth were inspected, found to have some few sharp points, and fixed with the floats. Finally her shoes were removed and reset in front, while her hind feet were rounded up at the edges so that they will not break off. Tonight she is out enjoying the grass of the paddocks along with an old pensioner. She will be kept up days and turned out nights till fall when she will join the barren mares for the winter. If turned out right now to hustle with the rest, our filly would soon be skin and bone. They have to be tapered off the grain.

JULY 23. It has been depressingly hot today and the horses have looked very tired in their stalls, some of them sweating freely. We had one horse to get a bit overcome with the heat while working in the corn. A couple of ounces of aromatic spirits of ammonia and frequent cold enemas soon brought him around, together with the comfortable treatment of playing a hose on him for half an hour or so. Some horses seem prone to overheating, and if once they get too hot they are likely to do so again. We always have the men take them easy in the hot weather and tell them to watch for horses that stop sweating.

JULY 25. A quiet day, with all the stock doing well with the exception of one of the saddle horses, which has for some reason developed a fever yet shows no symptoms of anything except a little dullness. As the fever went high tonight, I gave her a shot of neoarsphenamine in the jugular vein on general principles. This should knock the fever by tomorrow. Some glauber salts in water will help her, too.

JULY 26. Another violent storm with lots of rain late last night ended with a good cool morning, and I took the opportunity of taking a pleasant drive in my road cart to look over the horses in the stud, this time going clear up to the training stable and having a look at the yearlings, which are growing now with astonishing rapidity. Found all the horses in good order. Everywhere the grass is getting a good new start. If we have no bad luck fall pasturage should be good. The saddle horse is quite normal in temperature and seems to be quite well, though slow at eating. A physic ball appears indicated.

JULY 27. This has been a very busy day for us here. The dentist arrived this morning for the regular annual molar inspection of all the horses, which has been put off for three months. The stallions were gone over first, then the saddle horses, and after these were out of the way we got busy on the mares. All behaved remarkably well. Only two of the twenty head done had to be twitched. Some of the older mares needed little more than a light floating, but some that were new to the place were in bad shape and had a lot of work done. We find it pays to have all looked over annually, as they will do better and get more good out of their feed if they can masticate it as they should. Each of the stallions got a physic ball as well, and neither is feeling so bright tonight.

JULY 28. This morning it was the turn of the barren mares to get their dental inspection and at the same time we took 20 blood samples from the mares that were bred late and from those that were away for the season. These have gone over to the college tonight, and the rats will get the samples tomorrow. When we have the report on these last samples we should have a fair idea about the results of the past breeding season, though it is a far cry from now until all of the foals are here. The young mare that arrived here last week has passed a large number of long roundworms since having her physic ball and so we have drawn her today and she will get a worm pill in the morning to clear out the parasites, which, incidentally must be bad, for her tail is so itchy she cannot leave it alone.

JULY 29. From a gentleman in Puerto Rico came a sad note this morning asking for information about the vermifuge which I have used on foals prior to weaning—incidentally, I have had enquiries from Tulsa and Calgary, too, about this stuff. This breeder has had an epidemic of diarrhea which has swept his foals causing about a 50 per cent loss in his crop. This is the more unfortunate for they are the first crop from a young sire purchased in the States a couple of years ago, and the mares were gathered up here during the last several years. However, my friend and his partner are the kind of sportsmen who can "take it," and they will come back stronger than ever, I am sure. As I have never had an epidemic of this sort to handle, I have asked the editor to obtain information from the Kentucky

Agricultural Experiment Station for my correspondent. I would appreciate hearing from anyone who has had such an outbreak.

JULY 30. We got through with the dentist this morning, after he had spent three forenoons with us. I was surprised to see that eight of the older foals need a slight amount of attention. They had the sharp edges of their teeth smoothed off. After all the saddle stock had had their manes, tails, and ears trimmed up after lunch, I drove in the cart down to where the well diggers are putting in another artesian well, near the corral where the steers are kept in winter and whence the freeze caused us to move the beasts last January. We will have none of that trouble now, be the winter what it will, for the new well will take care of the water situation very well. It is about 250 feet deep and has a good flow of clear water continuously.

JULY 31. Spent a good part of a cool morning inspecting pasture land from the elevation of my road-cart and found that the land cut for hay is now well covered with our late summer and fall stand-by, lespedeza. The barren mares in the big field with the Madden shed are doing splendidly. If their looks mean anything not many of them will be in that lot next summer, but will be in the stables with foals at foot. The wheat threshing is now about finished. The men are filling up the spare stalls and all storage space at the home farm with straw so that it will not be necessary to haul it to us later on.

AUGUST 1. After the usual morning rounds of inspection, wherein I found all seemingly well, I went over to see the local Jersey Cattle Club show at our dairy, and an enjoyable show it was. There were about 60 head of cattle at the little affair and some of them, at least to my untutored eye, seemed to be very fine beasts. Our dairy manager seemed to be getting his share of ribbons though not too many, as befitted the host of the day. I noted that his fine old bull got the Grand Championship for bulls. Personally I would not care to handle this gentleman at all, and by the same token you can't get the dairy men into our stallions' stalls at any price.

AUGUST 2. Drove leisurely around the whole place this morning and in checking over the barren mares found that four were missing. An hour's search was necessary before they were discovered deep in the woods, quietly oblivious to anything but the quiet of the Sabbath. One of the older foals came in with a filled near hind leg, where she apparently had been kicked, below the hock. It is not bad, but we have rubbed it thoroughly with the 20 per cent icthyol ointment which we always keep on hand for such things. This, while unpleasant to use, is fine for almost any swelling.

AUGUST 3. They have been thrashing wheat in our fields at the home farm today and baling straw at the same time. The latter is being stored away in all the space we have available in lofts and empty stalls, so that we shall not have it to haul so soon next winter. The grain is going to be really worth something with the wheat market already well over the dollar mark. The crop is very good and remarkably clean of weed seed. As the farm headquarters are so far from here we are hosts tonight to about a dozen mules and workhorses, which look quite out of place in our box stalls. They do not approve of the change it seems, for they are making plenty of noise about it.

AUGUST 4. The heat today has been intense. This morning the blacksmith shod 10 of the mares in the big field in the comparative cool of the Madden shed. They very soon get the shoes loose when turned out this weather and need twice as much looking after as in the cool, flyless months. Have been filling out some more cards for the stallion index tonight. It is getting fuller all the time and I hope before long to have about all the sires in the country listed.

AUGUST 5. We had a good heavy downpour last night, just when it was badly needed in the pastures. It is still good and hot today, though. The mares and foals seem to mind the heat little just now, for some reason, and they are doing well.

AUGUST 6. Received the report on the last examinations made from the blood samples from the last lot of mares today. Of 16 mares whose blood was sent over, 12 are in foal. The other four were bred late and it was no surprise to know that they had not caught. One had lost a whacking big pair of twins last January and I have noted that mares that do this seem to be apt to skip breeding the next season. Another was a mare 24 years old which was hardly expected to get in foal. The report is certainly most encouraging.

AUGUST 7. As it was cool this morning we got in a good long ride through the pastures and all over the farm, seeing the barren mares out by the artesian well, where one of the men was cleaning out the trough with a broom and shovel. It now appears that only three mares will qualify for this location next year; they are due for some treatment this fall. The saddle ponies got some trimming up this afternoon, for all three of them will carry their youthful owners in the show-ring tomorrow. All the tack was well cleaned up and the leather looks good with the gloss of saddle soap well rubbed in. They have just brought the van down and set it. We will have a very early start, as the show is a half a hundred miles away or more.

AUGUST 8. A busy, full day well spent. Hustled around to see all in good order long before six this morning and loaded the three ponies for the road, before breakfast. Had a good morning at the horse show with two of the entries getting awards in strong competition, which was pleasing. Stopped in to see some score of Thoroughbreds at the farm of a man who specializes in patching up cripples and making broken down runners sound. There were all sorts and shapes on view, from many distant points, and, notwithstanding the strong odor of iodine paint and blisters, the visit was most interesting. I saw some X-ray pictures of a broken bone in the foot of a very good horse of a few years back. The latest pictures show how the fracture is healing from the bottom and demonstrate the value of the X-ray as an aid in diagnosis, when properly used. The pictures can fool one mightily unless one reads them right.

AUGUST 9. Busy this morning seeing all in order, which was done by driving 'round in the cool of the morning, with the horse and cart. Left home this evening, destination Saratoga. A tiresome trip with all night spent apparently getting nowhere. One becomes accustomed to too much comfort nowadays on the farm.

AUGUST 10. It looks as though every breeder of importance in the land is here enjoying the races and at the Sales paddocks this morning I have seen a great number of old friends inspecting the Kilmer yearlings, which are a good lot.

AUGUST 11. Spent the early hours of the morning at Surcingle, the private estate of Alfred Vanderbilt, saw many a fine-looking horse, including Discovery, which is in excellent condition. On the way to the Sales Paddocks was met by an old friend who has for 40 years exercised horses. Gave me the supposed winners of all the races. Five of them won, two at eight to one. Not being a betting man, I passed the good word along to a couple of friends, one of whom could not credit a farm lad with knowing anything. He lost on the day. Saw as fine a colt as one would want to see today. Sired by *Jacopo, a sure comer if ever there was one. If he is not overwhelmed by the other sires at Claiborne this horse will certainly make a mark in time to come. This is stronger praise than I am usually apt to give any untried sire.

AUGUST 12. After an all-night trip the green fields of Sleepy Hollow Stud looked mighty good this forenoon and despite leaving many a friend behind, it was a pleasure to be home again. Found on a leisurely and thorough inspection that all was well except with one foal which is not thriving as she should be. She will get an ounce of Gray's glycerine tonic morning and evening to see if it will bring her along as it usually does. And what a budget of welcome mail. Truly the best part of leaving the horses and the stud is to return to them.

AUGUST 13. Checking over the feet of all of the horses in the stud this morning, we found that a few of the mares needed re-setting. This was done, and about half of the foals' feet were trimmed. These latter are standing like old horses now and they are held in the cool alley-way of the barn where the breeze makes it decent for the blacksmith to work. Went up to the training stable and carefully considered the yearlings, in comparison with those seen at Saratoga. Ours looked very good to me, though lacking the flesh usually found on those at the sales. It looks to me that there were not as many over-fat horses there this year as I have often seen at Saratoga. I'm told that some I did not see went too much the other way for people to like them at all.

AUGUST 14. This has been one of those quiet off-days with little beyond the regular routine work of the stud farm going on. All the horses passed the usual morning and evening inspections and the men, after the manure was cleaned out and hauled away, have started hauling clay into the stables, filling in the low places which the horses' feet and the stable brooms have dug out. The clay is put into the holes after the latter have been dug up a bit with the mattock and wet down well. Lime is mixed plentifully with the clay so as to form a good solid compost which is almost like cement.

AUGUST 15. This being Saturday, we got the stable lawns all mowed and the edges of the gravel walks trimmed in preparation for the week-end. The edges seem to flourish when the grass grows nowhere else, and they need constant care to keep the place up to scratch. The men are all but one in town this afternoon, and it is very quiet on the farm. As soon as the man who comes on at four gets back, they will be turning out for the night, the man on all day having just finished feeding. The mares and foals are going at their feed. They get just what they eat with evident relish, leaving no crumbs behind.

AUGUST 16. A pleasant day with a delightful breeze which has made sitting under the trees in the garden a pleasure after the walk around the stables and inspection of the mares. Found a mare at the Madden shed which had been kicked well above the knee sometime last night. The men brought up water and disinfectant. After washing the leg off thoroughly we massaged it well with the icthyol ointment, 20 per cent strength. As she is not at all lame and the skin is only superficially opened we have not brought her down to the home farm, but we will do so if she does not progress as she should.

AUGUST 17. A blistering hot day with practically no air stirring anywhere. We had to get one of the stallions shod today, as he had stamped his fore shoe off. All but two nails were broken off right at the wall of the foot. The flies today have been worse than any day this year. The men say it means rain, but I'm inclined to doubt the accuracy of their forecasting of the weather. The injured mare was brought here for treatment today so that her wound could be washed off and her leg massaged with the icthyol ointment.

AUGUST 18. A much more pleasant day with a strong cool breeze from the northwest tempering the heat of the last few days. The cart came in for some use as I drove over all the pastures on an inspection tour. Rain is badly needed everywhere and the lawns and pastures are burning up. The last field of peas planted in July is not "making" at all but if we get rain soon it will be o. k. The mare from the Madden shed field which we brought down to the home place has gone back, as she is about well again. The mares in that lot are holding their condition very well, the lespedeza being their saving.

AUGUST 19. Hot and sticky again today. The farm crew have brought us a load of cow-peas which they are now housing at the upper farm and these will be fed to the mares and foals here for a change from their hay. They are very fond of them and there is much milk for the foals in this food. We hauled a couple of loads of the fresh straw and manure from the broodmare stalls up to the Madden shed today for bedding there. The cattle which run in that field pick it over and it makes a stamping place for the mares also. When the manure is hauled out it will have more value than if it were just piled up now and left until spring.

AUGUST 20. This has been a blistering hot day. As is usual when the weather gets so that the mares and foals break right for the woods as soon as turned out, we are having quite a few minor cripples. Two foals came in a trifle lame this morning. One had slightly wrenched the off hind ankle and one had had a kick on the front of the shin bone. The former was bathed for a while in hot water and then the ankle was rubbed with Absorbine an done up in sheet cotton and a derby bandage. The latter had her bruise rubbed with the old standby, icthyol.

AUGUST 21. Another day like yesterday, with the horses in the stables wringing wet all day. And do they take some watering while it is like this! They have the buckets full when they get in from the pastures—so called—and these are refilled an hour or so afterwards. Again at about

9 o'clock they want more, and again at 11. At one the buckets are all emptied of any water left in them and are wiped out, and fresh water goes in the stalls. Some need more by three but usually only one afternoon watering holds them until they go out, and then their first stop is the artesian well. The buckets are emptied on the shed and set upside down in the doorways until morning.

AUGUST 22. This has been another scorcher, but thanks to two storms, one last night and another this afternoon, things are a little better tonight. We had the ponies at another show today, returning before the heat cooked us all. At that, the ponies had to be washed and walked for a long time to cool them off on unloading. One silver cup and blue ribbon fell to our little riders in two classes, so we are all pleased.

AUGUST 23. It is a good thing there was no work to be done today for between the heat of the day and the biting of the flies we should have had little peace doing anything. Went around the horses early this morning and found all the minor cripples progressing as they should be. The foal which was hurt in the stifle has taken up the habit of chewing at his now healing wounds, so the man in charge of the granary, who is quite a hand at such things, has made a small cradle for the foal. This is a very satisfactory arrangement. This evening we turned out early so that the horses could get the benefit of the breeze. They lost little time in getting into the shade.

AUGUST 24. Riding with the young horsemen of the farm early this morning one could see already a marked improvement in the lespedeza in the big fields following the rains of Saturday. The farm crew is putting up some fine alfalfa in the barn at the upper farm where the weanlings will be stabled this fall. The crop is very good and the condition of it is just right for our purposes. We have put bandages on the ankles of two of the foals which were banged up a bit, as the swellings were not going away as quickly as they might. One foal paid no attention to the bandages, but the other soon ripped his off. The bandage was returned to the leg and dampened on the outside and a liberal coating of red pepper was sprinkled upon it. The result was that the foal tried only once to bother the bandage.

AUGUST 25. Flies were so worrisome today that it took three men to shoe a mare which had cast a shoe last night. One held the foal and two others knocked flies from the mare's legs for the blacksmith. At that, this has been a "good year" as far as flies go, with us.

AUGUST 26. This having been a lovely cool day and all being in order, we took some time off this afternoon to pay a couple of visits and to attend to some business some 50 miles from home. Found that the recent rains had helped grass and late crops everywhere and the prospect for fall pasture is now good. Saw some very nice yearlings, one particularly good filly by Jack High from a Man o' War mare, bred like the stakes winning filly High Fleet. It looks like a nick. I also saw some exceptionally large foals whose dams were much fatter than one usually sees them. In their stalls were great mounds of fresh alfalfa. Everyone reports an extremely scarcity of hay. This commodity is going to be highly expensive **next spring.**

AUGUST 27. A cool day with intermittent showers made it very pleasant again at Sleepy Hollow Stud. The rains have not penetrated at all, as we discovered when digging up some pipe lines to unchoke them. The ground is like cement a couple of inches down and one needs a mattock and bar to dig at all. Had a note from a reader of the Diary telling me about a promising 2-year-old that had fractured a bone in his foot, and asking me if I had any experience of this sort of thing. Yes, I have, too much of it, and the only thing that I saw do much good was to wait with all the patience in the world. Even then the patient may never be worth a quarter. Some of them get over the trouble in good shape while others are just "fini" as far as racing goes.

AUGUST 28. The horses thoroughly enjoy the change to cool weather. I spent most of the morning in my road cart driving around the farm and it was good to see the mares with their heads down, quietly grazing instead of sweltering in the sun. The grass is coming splendidly everywhere. Tonight I have been reading with great pleasure the new edition of Lieut. Col. John F. Wall's *Practical Light Horse Breeding.* The new edition covers some things left out previously and brings the former book up to date in many ways. Unique in its scope, the Wall book is the only American handbook for breeders which covers the whole field in concise fashion. It was first published in THE BLOOD-HORSE as a weekly feature and its success has been immense. No newcomer can afford to be without it, and it is invaluable to the oldster too.

AUGUST 29. As it was raining heavily at the time we were to load our ponies this morning, the youngsters missed their usual Saturday showing, much to their disappointment. The rain has continued off and on all day and the ground is getting the kind of a soaking it needed.

AUGUST 30. Due to the heavy rainfall last evening and the fact that a few of the foals have developed the slight colds that always seem to appear about this period of the year, we did not turn out last night at all, giving them a run in the paddocks early this morning. As it was quite cool they were able to stay out and have a good spell of grazing before being returned to their stalls for the day. The morning inspection was made by driving around all the pastures in the cart with the three youngsters and the terrier for company. The foals were· very inquisitive about the old Major and the cart, several of them coming around smelling the contraption from front to back, much to the enjoyment of the small fry in the vehicle. After we had been through the home paddocks we drove to the upper farm, stopping en route for a tour of the field with the dry mares in it. Finding all in good fettle we returned at a smart clip, getting home in time for a welcome breakfast. Sundays on a stud farm are enjoyable in a manner that poor townsmen can never appreciate.

AUGUST 31. Spent the majority of yesterday and last night, as well as this evening, reading carefully *The Breed of the Racehorse*, by Friedrich Becker. To my mind the book has some very sound lessons in it, though there is much that does not quite jibe. It is worth anybody's while to study winter nights, but is a little too tough for hot weather reading.

SEPTEMBER 1. This afternoon we were hosts to a couple of welcome visitors, an army officer whose books on breeding and bloodlines are well and favorably known, and an eminent physician who was the original developer of the blood test for pregnancy in mares. Everything came in for an inspection, somewhat hurried, to be sure, and the stallions, mares, and foals got some favorable criticism. As we stopped at the training quarters we saw the boys getting their tack in shape for the breaking of the yearlings which commences tomorrow.

SEPTEMBER 2. A sad duty came our way this morning. Our old pensioner broodmare passed away last night. Dam and grandam of many winners, she is gone but not forgotten. She was buried down with many another in the farm cemetery. Had the blacksmith down shoeing a dozen or so of the mares today, also had a couple of foals' feet trimmed at the same time. This evening it started to rain again just after we had the stock out, but we did not take them up.

SEPTEMBER 3. Went up to the training stable early this morning to observe the breaking of the score of yearlings which will now go into training for a few months. The men began with them yesterday, putting bridles and saddles—without stirrups—on them in the stalls and then mounting the boys quietly outside in a ploughed paddock. The yearlings took very quietly to all this and only two boys went off at all when the bucking began with the tightening of the girths. The whole proposition was handled with the minimum of noise and excitement and not one of the lot became worked up or excited. This morning the youngsters were mounted outside without a bit of trouble and in a few minutes were walking around the ring in the paddock. It was gratifying to see how quiet they were and the amount of confidence they had in everybody.

SEPTEMBER 4. After breakfast we drove up to the stables again to see the yearlings. They seemed to be going along very smoothly—not an obstreperous one in the lot, the trainer tells us. Back we came by way of the dry mares, and after inspecting them and noting the pasturage we decided on a bit of a grain ration for them. Each will get a gallon a day of mixed cracked corn and crushed oats, as they are all but three in foal and need the feed to nourish the one within.

SEPTEMBER 5. One of the foals came in this morning with a swollen ankle and this has had to be fomented with hot water and bandaged up in cotton. It is really surprising they do not get into more trouble than they do, the way they race and chase around. The yearlings were having trotting exercise when I stopped at the stables this morning and I tarried long enough to watch some of them getting their work. They are turned out in the early dews of the morning at four o'clock and come in when the men have the stalls all cleaned out about seven and then they go out for the saddle work. This turning out helps to keep them from getting too fresh and is a satisfactory proceeding from the lads' point of view.

SEPTEMBER 7. This has been a very busy day.
Our local community held its annual Horse Show
and Tournament about five miles from us and
we had five up there, getting a blue, a couple
of reds and two other ribbons so we are all well
pleased as the competition was keen. The class
of the horses in the show was much improved
on what it used to be, with the ever potent blood
of the Thoroughbred predominating everywhere
but in the saddle events.

SEPTEMBER 8. Inspecting the foals this morning I was struck by the way they grow first
in one spot and then in another. One big filly
out of a Man o' War mare was all front a month
ago with nowhere near as much development in
the quarters as we like and now she has shown
marked improvment towards growing up to her
forehand. One sees them differently almost each
time one looks at them and it is sometimes wise
not to see the horses too often. I think as a matter of interest that I shall measure them at the
withers and at the rump with the measuring cane
to see how much they really grow in a month and
where the growing is done.

SEPTEMBER 9. The horses came in from our
morning ride all wet and sticky and accordingly
were well washed off and scraped down before
being walked dry and watered off a little at a
time. The washing of them makes the groom's
work lighter, for it is a mean job to try to clean
properly a horse brought in gummy and sticky.
We have increased the rations that the mares and
foals get. Now the feeding is thrice daily and
the quantity is two gallons fed in mangers on
each side of the loose-box. The mixture used now
is four parts crushed oats and one part good
flakey bran. Four ounces of Enza-Vita goes with
each feed. This keeps the mares and foals in
fine healthy bloom and they seem to thrive well
on it.

SEPTEMBER 10. Blood poisoning can take a
tremendous hold on anything in a very short

time, as we learned today. One of the good fillies came in a couple of days ago with a very small, innocent-looking puncture of the skin midway between the knee and the shoulder on the inside of the leg. The wound was treated with disinfectants and irrigated regularly. By last night the leg had swollen to alarming proportions and tonight it is huge. The filly was treated with an intravenous injection and her leg had been constantly kept wet with a therapogen solution. Her appetite is fine, despite a temperature of 106 degrees.

SEPTEMBER 11. Tonight it looks as though our filly will make the grade, though her fever is still very high. She has been done up in cotton and bandages all round today to brace her good legs and to keep the flies from bothering her at all on the legs. She has had a couple of alcohol baths to freshen her up and we offer her fresh water hourly. She lay down last night for a few hours but has not been down today and is very tired tonight. Three intravenous injections of a powerful germicide have been given at eight-hour intervals and she should soon be turning the corner if her heart does not give in under the pressure. Her appetite is fine, though, and plenty of mineral oil keeps her bowels lubricated.

SEPTEMBER 12. After the crippled foal had been taken care of this morning—she is doing very well and looks past the crisis—I went up to the training stable to see how the yearlings were getting on. Found a set trotting around the race track in fine style. They were going just like a lot of old horses in training. The trainer tells me that they are an exceptionally good lot so far, but he thinks they may be storing up things for when they start to breeze. In the stable after the exercise I saw one filly standing with the shank over her back and no one holding her while she was washed off. The blacksmith has just finished plating the yearlings in front.

Hind shoes will probably not be put on before spring training starts.

SEPTEMBER 13. I found the swelling on the crippled foal's shoulder ready for opening this morning and this was done, much to the foal's relief. There was an awful lot of stuff in it that was better off out. Last night she went down and slept for several refreshing hours. The dry mares are doing better now that they get a grain ration as well as pasture. Some of the older foals look as if they'd be better off weaned and as soon as the "sign" is right they will be weaned.

SEPTEMBER 14. We had the blacksmith down at the stud today, shoeing a few of the mares and trimming foals. One of these had developed cracks running from the bottom of the wall in three hoofs up the center of the foot for a couple of inches. These we fired at the top of the cracks with a V-shaped iron which will effectively stop their going any further up towards the coronary band. I do not know why this particular filly developed these cracks, for sire and dam are both sound-footed animals and the condition is quite rare. Filing in a straight line across the top of the cracks possibly would have done the trick, but the firing, though taking longer and being a more unpleasant job, is really more effective.

SEPTEMBER 15. More shoeing of mares today, this time at the upper farm. This morning we sent the van and a truck some hundred-odd miles for a couple of dozen Aberdeen Angus calves which are turned out in the big paddock with the mares at the upper farm. They are a nice tame lot and will be in the corrals to utilize the old bedding from the stables this winter. There will be plenty of corn fodder for them also.

SEPTEMBER 16. We took the mare with the crippled foal out this morning for a bit of a sunning while her stall was cleaned out and both appreciated the outing a lot. The foal is going very much sounder now; the swelling is almost gone and her temperature normal. Drove up to the training quarters to see the yearlings which are now galloping a mile daily. Already one sees the middles disappearing and the loins filling up with more muscle.

SEPTEMBER 17. All day the clouds have been banking in the northeast, and all day the farm gang have been working like Trojans getting the soy bean hay into the new barn up by the training stable. They brought us a load this evening to tide us over till our barn is filled again, which should be soon if the rain does not interfere. The horses certainly like the soy beans much better than they do the cow-peas. I suppose the former are not as tough. The new names of the yearlings came back with the approval of The Jockey Club this morning and we have some well named youngsters, I think, judging from the list turned over to me. We are in good time with the naming this year. It usually takes an awful time to get the names through. The crippled foal continues to do very well indeed, and it is really astonishing what a recovery she has made.

SEPTEMBER 18. Tonight all the horses are indoors with the exception of the dry mares whose hay rack has been filled up in case they decide to stay in the shed. The storm warnings have been coming in all day, but it looks now as though the hurricane that has been desolating the seaboard is turning out to sea and will miss us. The mares and foals are resting well, enjoying the deep straw beds for a change. The dentist has been here working on the teeth of the yearlings this afternoon. He got about ten of them done and almost every other one had the wolf teeth that must be taken out.

SEPTEMBER 19. The hurricane has passed us by, and today has been lovely, except that the flies missed eating yesterday and made up for it this morning. We turned everything out for a

run early today but by nine all were in again.
Got all the troughs cleaned out this morning, particularly that which the new lot of steers had
used as a footbath. These last are a nice even
lot and are quite at home with the mares and
foals. The last field of soy bean hay is being
cut and it is to come here for our mares and
foals this winter. Had the little crippled foal out
with the rest this morning. I never saw anything recover faster when it did start. A therapogen irrigation is a wonderful healer.

SEPTEMBER 20. The unlucky Man o' War filly
which has just got thoroughly well after being
cut down last spring came in this morning with
a very lame off fore leg. All indications point to
a wrench of the ankle as the cause of the trouble, which does not look like being much. Tonight
we have beein going over the foals considering
the question of weaning or waiting a while.
There's another week yet till the "sign" is right.

SEPTEMBER 21. Very busy today cleaning the
stables of the usual extra lot of manure that is
part of Monday's lot due to the easy Sunday, and
this we hauled up to the Madden shed for bedding. There is a bunch of young Jerseys in that
field now and they get some feed out of the straw
as well as the mares using it for bedding. Got a
call from a near neighbor who had a fine young
riding horse which was very lame. Investigation
showed that the horse had been cast and had
thrown out the stifle of his off hind leg. We
worked on it awhile but made little headway until
one of my men, who is very large and strong,
came along. Taking the fetlock in his hand, he
quickly snatched the leg upwards and flexed it
inward at the same time. The stifle went back
into place all right but the colt is still very sore.
He will be fomented with hot water and Epsom
salts to take the soreness out of the joint.

SEPTEMBER 22. No sooner is one cripple on the
way to recovery than there's another of some
sort crying for attention. This time it's a work

horse. She pulled a shoe during the Sunday vacation at grass and she must have stepped on one of the nails before the shoe was found hanging and was pulled off Sunday night. The smith shod the mare Monday but today she was very lame and on the shoe being taken off I found that there was quite a pus pocket where the nail had pricked. This got the usual treatment of cauterization with iodine crystals and turpentine and the foot was poulticed with hot flax-seed. The mare got the usual 1,500-unit dose of tetanus antitoxin.

SEPTEMBER 23. The crippled mare is much easier today but her poultice was renewed for another day. All feed rations have been cut in half at the home farm now, as they have hauled some of the soya beans to us and there is a lot of grain in the pods. The hay is very rich and it is much the best to go light on the grains when feeding this roughage.

SEPTEMBER 24. Today we moved the steers and dry mares from the Madden shed field to another field nearer where there was a grain crop with new grass coming on. The pasture there is very good and both mares and steers ought to do well on it. Both stallions were shod this morning and some of the dry mares also. A letter came today from my Puerto Rican correspondent who had such bad luck with white scour in his stud. Thanks to the information supplied him by the Kentucky Agricultural Experiment Station he was able to check and overcome the disease without too much mortality. He writes me that he is moving his entire stud to high land well inland.

SEPTEMBER 25. Sent into town this morning for our van which has been adorned with a new coat of paint and trimmings. The appearance of this valuable article is thus much improved.

SEPTEMBER 26. This has been a busy day indeed. Drove 65 miles this morning to attend a meeting of our state horse breeders' association

and then drove 35 miles across country to fulfil
an engagement to judge a horse show.

SEPTEMBER 27. Had the pleasure of inspecting
the course and plant of William du Pont, Jr., at
Fair Hill today and was astonished to see the
tremendous height of the jumps on the course
where the race that bids fair to become America's Grand National was run last Saturday. Mr.
du Pont was host to a score or so of Turf writers
and showed movie films which were taken of the
races. As one of the winners was bred at the
Sleepy Hollow Stud, this phase of the entertainment was most interesting. We watched the
horse come from behind to win a 15-furlong race
with his ears pricked. This same horse was cut
down in a stakes two years ago the tendon of
the off hind leg was severed.

SEPTEMBER 28. The "sign" is getting right now
for the weaning, so today we have had all the
foals' feet looked over so that when they start
pawing and fussing a bit tomorrow they will not
be able to break them up. Also the mares have
been fed nothing much since yesterday so that
they may not have quite as much milk to be
taken from them. That is some job in many
cases. The stalls are all prepared by now for
the mares at the upper farm, while the foals
which tomorrow will become "weanlings" are to
be stabled two in a stall for a couple of weeks
or so at the home farm. Thus, with three miles
separating them, the mares and foals will not be
able to answer each other's cries. Putting the
little ones together in twos for a while breaks
some of the shock for them.

SEPTEMBER 29. It is most fortunate we weaned
today, for tonight we have a real old northeaster
on hand and it is very unpleasant. We led the
mares to the upper farm this morning, leaving
their foals here, 11 in the lot. Then we led down
15 mares and their foals from the upper farm
and put the youngsters in stalls here, immediately
returning the dams to their previous location,

except that all went into different stalls. The eight colts are in one stable, occupying four stalls. The 16 fillies we have decided to keep after weeding out a couple are in eight stalls in the other barn. They are all doing well and are very quiet tonight. They have feed boxes in two corners of the stalls so that there is little or no scrapping and as the rations have been kept short for a couple of days the foals are eating well, being hungry. The mares we milked this evening, leaving just a little there. The udders were greased well with a mixture of one ounce of fluid extract of belladonna in a quart of camphorated oil. The mares are all in single stalls with plenty of plain hay and water but they will have no grain for some time. They, too are quiet. They can say what they like about the "sign." If we wean when the sign is "in the leg" it is my considered opinion that the foals worry less and do better all round. There's nothing to lose by it and all to gain. I may be old-fashioned, but I'm a sign believer.

SEPTEMBER 30. Wading around through the rain and mud today, my belief in the efficacy of the "sign" was strengthened more than ever. Never in many years have the weanlings commenced their independent existence with a better start. Last night, despite listening and a couple of trips around the yard with the watchman, I heard very little noise, and this morning the buckets were all about empty, the feed mangers were bare, and almost all of the rack of mixed clover hay was gone. The weanlings did well at noon also and there has been no pawing and worrying. A few of the mares had taut udders this morning and a few again this afternoon. They, too, seem to be faring all right.

OCTOBER 1. The foals are settling down very well and it is a treat to see how they are cleaning up their feed. We do not feed them all they want at all times, though. They are fed three times a day, at 5 a. m., 11 a. m., and 5 p. m. Each gets four quarts in the morning and at night and two at noon of a mixture of four parts crushed oats and one part bran, with a couple of ounces of Enza-Vita. This is cut down in the case of those that do not clean it up right away. They have plenty of fresh water at all times. This morning we went over the mares' udders and found three that were rather full and these were stripped out well. The rest had practically nothing in them and so were only anointed with the oil.

OCTOBER 2. This morning I went up to the upper farm early and saw the mares' bags gone over before we turned them out. They were in good order and went out without much racing around. We divided them into three lots and put each lot of mares in separate small paddocks so that if they did want to run they could not go far. They will stay out until tomorrow morning and then will be examined again. The foals we turned out also for about three hours this morning in two small stallion paddocks. They grazed around a bit but did little fussing and were caught pair by pair and were returned to their stalls without incident. Only two of the fillies look at all drawn amidships and we are well pleased with their actions so far. These weanlings will continue to be brought in for an hour and a half at mid-day in order that each may get its proper food, and also they get a better opportunity to rest, as youngsters should.

OCTOBER 3. All mares whose foals were weaned were brought in for inspection this morning, but only about three or four of them had to be milked before they were put out into a big meadow where they will get a few weeks to "cool out" from any grain feeding before being put in their winter quarters. The weanlings have been out all day, just coming in for the noon feed. One of them was very lame this morning and investigation showed that the toe of her off fore foot was worn so that a stone had worked itself up into the space between the inner and outer walls of the foot. We cut it out and poulticed the foot and the little filly is much easier to-night.

OCTOBER 4. A busy Sunday with a large number of visitors, brought out by the lovely fall weather. Looked over the mares early this morning and they made a nice picture, all those that were weaned in one big field, strung out against the skyline. They are quite content and have no appearance of distended udders. The weanlings went out about eight this morning and stayed out until 3:30 p. m. They, too, are quiet and did a good deal of grazing. On Sundays they do not get a noon feed but come in early in the evening. They are all filling out nicely and they drink a lot of water, which is always kept fresh and clean before them.

OCTOBER 5. This morning we took all of the weaned mares in for an examination of their udders and for the blacksmith to check over their feet. Half a dozen or so were trimmed or shod, as was needed, and four had some milk drawn from them. They went out again as soon as these jobs were attended to and will not be brought up for about three days now unless any of them look as though they need attention in the meanwhile. The men at the upper farm are getting the stables well cobwebbed and generally furbished up in preparation for winter; they are digging up the stall floors where they are uneven and are filling up the holes with clay and lime. The 16 weanling fillies will go up there in a few weeks, as soon as they are well over the initial stage of weaning and are ready for separation into single stalls.

OCTOBER 6. Went up to officiate as judge of a few classes of horses at a students' judging contest held at a nearby city and the tough part was to grade the boys on their reasons for their placings. Obviously many of the lads had not had the opportunity of seeing the different types of animals used and were trying to fit classroom phrases to the horses shown. It is a pity all agricultural colleges do not have available for use all breeds of horses. This morning we clipped the saddle ponies whose long coats made it hard to cool them out decently after exercise. The ponies certainly look a great deal better for the clipping and doubtless feel better too.

OCTOBER 7. One of the new weanlings, a filly, had a bad case of flatulent colic this morning and was bloated like an old cow full of green clover. She had two half-ounce capsules of aromatic spirits of ammonia and one of chloral hydrate also before she got relief. She was also washed out per rectum with an injection of soapy water and linseed oil. I drove up to see the yearlings galloped this morning and was much pleased with the way in which they are going. They got a two-mile gallop and went at their work with a vim and the style of old horses, coming back and standing in front of the stand where the boys dismounted and walked them quietly to the stable. As it was a sticky, sultry morning, it took some time to cool them out properly but our trainer always has this done very thoroughly. One the way home I had a good look at the mares we weaned last week and found them all in good shape, standing around enjoying the breeze on a high place in their big field. So far none shows any ill effects from the discontinuance of the grain ration.

OCTOBER 8. Today we have been building a fence around a new paddock for a stallion. The paddock in question being much too large for one horse, we have divided it in half, with a stout double fence of creosoted lumber five feet high. Aided by a visiting fireman in the shape of the associate editor of this magazine, we weighed and measured the weanlings this afternoon, for the first time. Twenty-four were measured and the average height was 13 hands and an inch. In weights they varied from 440 pounds to 620 pounds. These heights and weights are those of foals just eight days weaned and all but one foaled between March 1 and

May 1. Two detached ramps afforded the means of access to and egress from the scale platform, which has a rail on each side so the foals will not slip off. Strips of old belting afford good foot-holds. In all the lot we did not have one that gave us any trouble getting on or off the scales.

OCTOBER 9. This morning our visitors accompanied us on our round of inspections, winding up at the training stable, where we watched the gallops of the yearlings. Thence we betook ourselves for a bit of racing, despite vile weather with intermittent showers and sticky humidity.

OCTOBER 10. I went up to the stable this morning, as our yearlings were slated for breezing today, but the heavy showers of last night had left the track in a condition that precluded all thought of any speed work at all. There is lots of time yet, however, for speed trials, though these are never overdone with us. As there was nothing going on there, we left early for the show of breeding stock that our local community has sponsored for the past four years. In the earlier years the quality of the draft and saddle stock was not much to brag about, but all that is changed now. Today we had no less than 75 entries in the heavy classes and well over a score of light breeds, chiefly mares suitable to produce hunters and young stock of various ages. These local shows are the finest things to stimulate interest in better livestock of all breeds.

OCTOBER 11. Had a very pleasant drive this morning in the roadcart with our stallion groom. Starting off at the lower end of the farm, we inspected mares, weanlings, pasturage, and fences, winding up at home after a good eight miles. The mares are doing splendidly on the good grazing with the big steers up at the upper farm and there is no indication of any feeding being needed for them. The weanlings are getting along all right, too, but it is about time for them to go into their single stalls and a few of

them look as though a bit of worming might
help them. This requirement will soon be attended to. Grazing is fair now, inasmuch as
recent rains have dampened things after a record
dry September whose burning winds scorched
the grass lands badly. All the corn is cut and in
the shock and the barley is in, with the winter
wheat planting well under way, and soon the
honking of the wild geese on their southward
trek will be heard in the night.

OCTOBER 12. It has been a good deal cooler
today. The saddle horses feel good these cool
mornings, and today one of our young riders
had a fair walk home due to his mount getting
too fresh. The pony preceded her rider to the
stable by some time. Days like this, one can
really enjoy driving around on inspection with
the horse and cart, and the old Major seems to
have taken on new vigor since it got cooler.
We shod the old lad today and then I drove him
to the upper farm to look the mares over. They
were ensconced in deep woods which, unfortunately, they were chewing on considerably. We
will have to paint the stripped parts of the
trees with tar or else we will lose them. On our
way home we stopped to watch the seeding outfit beginning to put the winter wheat into the
ground. Another team has been mowing off the
paddocks at the home farm, this having been
put off until the corn was in and the men and
teams had time for work which is not so timely.

OCTOBER 13. The weanling fillies are a trifle
lonesome tonight inasmuch as they have been
shipped to the upper farm, where they have gone
into single stalls. The van was stalled for two
horses abreast and two weanlings went into each
stall. They had room enough and they helped
brace each other. Only one gave us trouble, and
she distinguished herself by squealing exactly
like a hog while being loaded. One other showed
all the kicking ability of a football player but
a twitch settled her. We did not hurry them at

all and the shipping of the 16 was without incident, the little ones unloading as easily as they went on. For a few brief moments I took time out from shipping to watch a couple of sets of yearlings get their first breeze in earnest. They looked mighty good to me, crying to run in most cases, but wisely restrained.

OCTOBER 14. Vanned the weanling colts us to the training stable this afternoon and put them into their single stalls up there. They soon settled down to the new surroundings..

OCROBER 15. I rode up to the upper farm about dawn this morning to see how the weanling fillies were doing and to watch them go out. All the feed boxes—the night watchman feeds them at 4:30 a. m. now—were clean as a whistle and the water buckets showed that the youngsters were drinking as they should. The hay racks were appreciably depleted also. All of which indicates that we did right in separating the youngsters into single stalls. I noticed a couple of them going after the round salt blocks which are in each feed box, and which do not get stuck in a corner for food to accumulate around. The weanlings went out into a couple of small handy paddocks and galloped around in good shape when loosened. From the upper farm I traveled to the training stable where the yearlings were working and saw a good-looking set of colts work an easy quarter-mile in pairs. They shape as though they would be ready for the asking of the important question very soon.

OCTOBER 16. A dull, unpleasant sort of a day with rain in the offing. Drove around inspecting the mares this morning and found the 23 up at the upper farm deep in the woods and as somnolent as aldermen. They certainly look as though the "cooling out" from grain feeding is doing them well. All the lot are supposedly in foal, and they show every indication of it. It is very quiet at the home farm now, for there is not a stall in use other than those occupied by the five saddle horses and the head sire. There are some 15 more mares down here, but they are in a big field below the buildings where they have the woods for shelter. The men are giving the place its final trimming up before the winter, getting all the cobwebs out of the corners and the grass trimmed, etc.

OCTOBER 17. The yearlings got some exercise and breezing in the mud today for it rained heavily last night. Some trainers leave their horses in under such circumstances, or else they just gallop them. I recall the late John Gallaher having the best lot of mudders in the Middle West in days gone by, and he seemed to delight in breezing and working them in the bad going. Went racing this afternoon to see our Breeders' Futurity run for but the bad going rather robbed the race of interest. Saw a horse that was badly cut down behind, so much so that the tendon had been stripped down and a pocket of useless skin was left. Discussing with the trainer the advisability of trying to sew the skin back, we came to the conclusion that it was best in such a case to cut the skin off completely and to let the leg grow a new skin. The loose skin would only become necrotic anyway, and it would be a worse mess in the long run.

OCTOBER 18. Dodging showers this morning, I betook myself in the road cart on a drive around the farm, inspecting all the mares and weanlings. One of the latter has developed an arthritis lameness and we have put her on iodide of potash, as well as on some salts mixture in order to cure the lameness, which has affected the shoulders worst, from within. The filly is getting some Gray's Glycerine Tonic as well, and we are hopeful that she will throw off the trouble before long for she is one of the best-bred ones in the lot. The weanlings seem to be doing very well, bar one or two which have not appreciated their single standard of living. The mares continue to do well out, and the longer we can leave them where they are the better it will suit our hay and feed supplies. Fall grasses are coming along well now in all the paddocks, and I see the farm crew is well along in the wheat planting.

OCTOBER 19. This has been shipping day with us. First thing this morning we sent off three mares that had been sold in a van with a 600-mile trip ahead of them. They were well bedded, and plenty of hay was sent with them. Two are in foal and one is not and it's a pretty long run for them, more of a run than I like as far as in-foal mares are concerned, though it's all right for the barrens. These mares had to make the trip with nobody but the driver aboard the van, which is running a bit of a risk. It's cheap insurance to pay a man to ride with mares, for nobody can tell when they'll throw a car-fit or get thrown down when one of these fancy drivers cuts in close. After these had left we sent a mare and foal to the railroad for a 1,500-mile trip by freight. They went alone also, but they had a barrel of water fixed in the corner. The car was divided in half to make a big box stall. Also they were well and solidly built in with two-by-sixes, and two bales of hay were packed in front of them, with the wires taken off. Shipping by the B. & O., they had the advantage of an excellent livestock department, which keeps close tabs on them when requested to.

OCTOBER 20. Today the blacksmith has had in all the mares whose foals were weaned and he now has half of them shod. They all needed some attention and all seem to be doing splendidly as far as bodily condition goes. If the present good weather continues they will be out there for some time yet. The weanlings, too, seem to be shaping up as they should. All but a very few are thriving splendidly. Yesterday the blacksmith took the shoes off the saddle ponies, for it is school time again and their young riders have to heed the call of the classroom. The ponies now have tips on in front and they are bare behind and are turned out all day, getting a modicum of grain.

OCTOBER 21. We've a new stallion here today and there's plenty of attention for him. All the farm finds business for a few minutes at the stud. The sire, a perfect gentleman in every respect, yawningly takes it all as his due. On arrival late last night he inspected his new quarters, and, finding them suitable, lay down and slept for a few hours in perfect peace. He's entitled to rest after an arduous trip. This morning he was led around his new paddock and turned loose for a run which he enjoyed.

OCTOBER 22. Arrived at the Lexington sales this morning and found a mare that looked good enough to be at Sleepy Hollow Stud, so there she will go in a day or two. Went racing at Keeneland with the editor of this journal in the afternoon, and what a spot it is! Conceived long ago in the mind of John Oliver Keene, this vision has now become a reality, not quite as Jack had originally intended, perhaps, yet in a form that augurs well for the future. Was surprised at the cosmopolitan crowd I saw at the track and it seemed as though everyone one ever knew was on hand and bent on offering Kentucky's traditional hospitality. May the vision of those who are responsible for Keeneland never dim, for they have done their job splendidly.

OCTOBER 23. Last night I attended the Thoroughbred Club's annual dinner. A delightful affair it was, honoring a true Kentucky gentleman. This morning I paid homage to the finest collection of stallions, I suppose, that has been on one stud farm at one time in many a long year. Led by the Derby winner *Blenheim II, the parade of these sires occupied a couple of well-spent hours and it was educational in the extreme to examine them at leisure. I also saw some very good weanlings this morning by Wise Counsellor, Jamestown, and *Jacopo, of whose success I repeat my conviction. These were at the farm of a Bourbon county breeder who was mine host for the night.

OCTOBER 24. Arrived home this morning, found everything in good order. The newly arrived sire is now out all day and as happy and contented as though he had spent years instead of days with us. The other stallions and the weanlings came in for a brief inspection, the mares also. They will get a close and leisurely going over tomorrow morning.

OCTOBER 25. Writing this date reminds me of an almost—and willingly—forgotten birthday. There have been quite a number of visitors here to see our new sire this afternoon, among them a prominent breeder whose colors have been carried in many victories in days gone by. I inspected one and all of the horses of various ages in my charge today and came to the conclusion that while the weanlings showed improvement in the past week there were several of the mares that definitely had gone back in condition and that need some feed besides the grass, which has not much food value just now.

OCTOBER 26. Our new broodmare arrived this morning and on inspection we liked her better than when she was purchased. All my crew and a couple of the farm gang, whom we borrowed, have been busy moving stock around today, in a cold, misty rain, and with all signs pointing to a stretch of bad weather on hand. The results of our labors are that here at the home farm there are 20 in-foal mares, the two stallions, and The Major, which is used all year either driving or under saddle. At the Madden shed are the three barren mares, four ponies, two maiden mares, a young half-bred and her old pensioner dam, rather a mixed crew. At the upper farm is another stallion and there, too, are 17 more in-foal mares and a dozen weanling fillies, the rest having joined the weanling colts at the training stable.

OCTOBER 27. Last night the wind veered to the northwest and the mercury dropped 30 degrees or so, and today it has been unseasonably cold.

Both of our chief stallions were photographed this morning, and some job it was to get them just right. We worked on one before lunch, then knocked off for the meal and a rest. The other did better after we ourselves were in better fettle. These photographers deserve a lot of praise for the excellent work they do, for a Thoroughbred stallion is far from a patient subject, as a rule.

OCTOBER 28. There was something of a battle today when a couple of mares ganged up on another and belted her high, wide and handsome. Curiously, they had all been together for long periods before with no trouble. Tonight the poor old victim is so sore she can hardly walk, so many are her bruises and bumps. We fomented her well with plenty of hot water and then massaged her with the old standby, the icthyol ointment, which we rubbed well into all of her bruises. As cold as it is, she's going to be in misery for a day or two and we shall have to watch her closely to see if she loses her foal as a result of her tribulations.

OCTOBER 29. The victim of the assault and battery case among the mares yesterday is today a great deal easier, thanks to hot water fomentations and liberal use of icthyol ointment. Though it was very cold here this morning with a crisp white frost, it was a good deal pleasanter this afternoon, so the mare and a quiet companion shared a small paddock for an hour or two. She'll be all right in a day or two now. Took our new sire out for a look at the farm today. He jogged along for about eight miles behind the road cart in which I was riding, his groom leading him, and apparently thoroughly enjoyed the outing. Nothing in the world upsets his equanimity and he now runs out as he chooses night and day, his box being in his paddock. The weanlings are noisy and sad-looking tonight, for they are in empty stalls with nothing but their water buckets. Tomorrow they'll be treated for worms, each getting a dose of carbon tetrachloride followed by glauber salts. The new stallion will get a ball and will have his teeth fixed at the same time while the veterinarian is here.

OCTOBER 30. Well, our poor weanlings and ourselves got badly fooled, for our veterinarian got in a jam as a witness in an accident case, so we got no worming done this day, and we'll have it all to go through with again on Monday. The foals were well tucked up too, sad to say. As all were perforce indoors we finished up with the registration applications. Of course we really should have done this sooner but the deadline is October 31 and the foals change their colors so much as they grow older that one usually awaits the last moment before finally finishing the job. Twenty-five blanks had to be filled in, and it is good to note that there's going to be a deal less of misapprehension about who bred a horse, now that there is a separate line for this information in the blank, and it is clearly stated that the owner of the mare at the time of the foal's birth is the breeder of the foal. Of course we breeders do not all agree with this rule for it seems to me that the man whose brain conceived the mating of the sire and dam of a great horse, and then had bad luck and had to sell his mare while in foal, is entitled to the lion's share of the credit for breeding the horse.

OCTOBER 31. In the mail today comes a note from an eastern breeder who last spring lost a good foal from a 9-year-old mare due to the mare's not allowing her foal—her first one—to nurse at all. My correspondent asks me how I would have handled the situation. He had tried a foster mother and raising the foal by hand. Well, in the first place the mare apparently had no maternal instincts from some cause. Now it sometimes occurs that old mares do not take to motherhood well, though this condition is rare in my experience. Then often a mare will sometimes have a tightly distended udder that causes her great pain when the foal tries to nurse her, and if she is new at the game that makes it worse. If the udder seems to be taut it is wise to hold up the near fore leg and draw some of the milk gently from the mare to soften the udder, massaging that organ the while with the milk. If the mare will not allow the foal near her then, put a twitch on her and hold her thus until the foal can give her a good rooting over, holding up the fore leg at the same time. This may have to be done for a day or two while the foal sucks but it will not be long usually before the mare comes around as she should. If the mare will not let the foal suck and the little one is losing heart, draw some of her milk into a clean warm pan and put a nipple on a baby's bottle and try to feed it that way; it's inconvenient and a slow job, I'll admit. The milk can be strengthened by the addition of a well beaten up egg and a dash of whiskey. It's important that the foal should not be allowed to get weak. As to the foster mother, if one is available, she will be invaluable, but first get some of her milk and feed the foal on it for a feed or two and rub the mare's milk on the foal's face and tail so that she will get the smell. If the foster mother has just foaled, take her placenta, or afterbirth, and wrap it around the foal you want her to take, and there should not be much difficulty, but take no chances of her kicking the foal. It's by scent, not sight, that mares know their offspring.

NOVEMBER 1. Another busy Sunday showing off the stallions and mares. The weanlings have been drawn again tonight and will be treated in the morning, if all goes according to plan. Brought my Stallion Register up to date by inserting the new names of the yearlings in their dams' sheets, also adding the welcome word "winner" behind a couple more of the 2-year-olds' names. With the invaluable help of the little book, *Sires of American Thoroughbreds*, I typed up sheets for the two new mares that have joined the stud.

NOVEMBER 2. The weanlings got their treatments today in short order. It took us but 45 minutes to finish up the 13 at the upper farm and 35 at the training stable for the dozen there. The stomach tube was used and the foals got 24 c. c. each of carbon tetrachloride followed by a quantity of a glauber salts solution which varied according to the size of the patient from 24 to 20 ounces. They stayed in for an hour or so and then were turned out while the stalls were bedded and the hay racks filled, also their buckets were refilled. Tonight all appear to be well and in good order. The watchmen at each place will be observing the weanlings closely and it will not be surprising if we get a call.

NOVEMBER 3. The salts are working on the weanlings this evening and the worms are coming from almost all of the patients. One colt is uneasy and has not purged. He has had a good dose of mineral oil mixed with a warm water solution of a tablespoonful of chloral hydrate. Of course he's the best colt we have, but he'll be all right by morning, I think. This morning we were hosts to the Mexican Army Horse show team, which group of excellent horsemen was paying its first visit to an American breeding farm. After lunch we betook ourselves to Pimlico where we saw once more the farcical thing of a breeder-owner's years of effort thrown away by the lack of control of a jockey who apparently was unable to resist an impulse to foul another horse, and so marred for thousands a grand horse race in the Pimlico Futurity.

NOVEMBER 4. Up and around the stock in good time this morning with a hundred-odd-mile drive ahead of us to attend a sale of Thoroughbreds that promised some bargains which materialized all right when we got there. A lot of cheap stuff that brought nothing cluttered up the catalogue, but it appeared that horses brought what they were worth in most cases. On return tonight we stopped to see the colt that was under the weather last night and found him shaping up finely. At both places the men report a good crop of worms.

NOVEMBER 5. It has been bitterly cold, with a stiff northwest breeze. The farm crew, well along with the husking of the corn, has been filling in one side of the hayloft at the Madden shed with shredded fodder which will be used in the rack for feed, and for bedding as well, when the black steers are there. The fodder is a bright green and is as dry as can be, in fine shape for putting indoors. Two fillies came in this morning, retired to the breeding paddock. A 3-year-old and a 2-year-old, both are fairly well wound up, and so, to help unwind them and to cool them out, each has had a physic ball this afternoon. We will not turn them out into the shed right away, giving them time to get over the change from training. The weanlings are pretty well back to normalcy now and the worms seen are fewer. About 80 per cent showed parasites.

NOVEMBER 6. The yearlings this morning were getting a sharp and short "blow-out" for their trials, which will be held Sunday, November 8. We expect quite a crowd here on that day and I have been busy this evening making some new rope shanks to show the mares and weanlings with. We use ⅝-inch white cotton rope, as this outlasts manila by far, and it never hardens when wet. Nor—most important—will cotton rope burn the hand when a horse lunges away. We cut the rope into convenient lengths, about five feet when finished, and splice a good sized swivel snap on one end. The other is whipped fast with cord, so that it will not unravel. Had one of our very infrequent minor colic cases this afternoon. An old mare this time. She soon rounded to when she was given an enema of linseed oil, soap, and water and a dose of colic mixture.

NOVEMBER 7. This morning we sent the old steers up to the upper farm where they will be fed for the market. In place of them we receive

Monday a draft of eight from• the last lot of calves, purchased a month or more ago. These will be impounded in the corral where they can run on the straw manure from the broodmares' stalls. This evening we had an enjoyable drive in the cart through the fields where the mares run and through the corn fields where everybody in the neighborhood is busy husking corn on piece-work. They are making things hum and the fodder is fast going into our loft at the shed.

NOVEMBER 8. Rain commenced to fall as soon as we had the horses out this morning so they soon returned within doors. The track was dulled somewhat, also, when we worked the yearlings. Only a dozen worked, six sets of two each, as some of the others have bucked their shins. We had quite a crowd on hand and showed off our breeding stock after lunch, despite the rain, which fell all afternoon. One of our guests was from France, where he had charge of our head sire during his racing career, also managing him at stud for a couple of seasons or so. The gentleman expressed himself delighted with the appearance of his erstwhile charge, though, as is usual with these highfalutin .sires, the horse apparently did not recognize his old master.

NOVEMBER 9. A welcome addition to my small library in the shape of Harry Disston's *Equestionnaire*, arrived this morning and I have spent a couple of hours tonight scanning its contents. Arranged in chapters under various headings are several hundred questions. The answers are listed in the second section of the book.

NOVEMBER 10. At the training stable this morning I saw a few of the yearlings breezed. They have commenced bucking, and the trainer wants them to do their bucking properly so as to have it all over with. Those which have already started to buck have their shins done up in antiphlogistine for a few days until the fever is out of the legs and then they will be thoroughly blistered with our pet remedy, Irish

Reducine. This stuff, while not pleasant to handle, is yet effective and the juveniles will be blistered from knee to coronet with it. The great advantage of using this remedy, which must be well rubbed in the first time used, is that horses can be turned out with the stuff on their legs. They may get some on their noses and face, but no ill effects will be seen. No bandages are needed.

NOVEMBER 11. Took our new sire for a long drive around the countryside this morning. He traveled along gaily behind us in the road cart. The big lad loves these jaunts, which afford him infinitely better exercise than the longeing line he has been accustomed to. The longe line method is severe on horses' hocks and ankles.

NOVEMBER 12. A dull miserable sort of day with intermittent cold showers that made us keep the stock indoors. The blacksmith has been over the feet of the mares and weanlings, shoeing some of the former and trimming all of the latter. The weanlings are doing very well now and one can see a marked improvement in their condition in the past couple of weeks. We'll weigh them in a couple of days or so. Have been getting the copy ready for our stallion advertisements tonight, these usually being run from December on for three months. It is quite an interesting job tracing out the various winners and statistics about the get of the horses. It is well worth the trouble and keeps one posted.

NOVEMBER 13. Drove up to the training stable in the cart this morning and had a look at the yearling and weanling divisions now up there. The former all received a physic ball yesterday and the physic was working this morning, some of the patients feeling pretty miserable. A number of them have already been blistered well with the Irish Reducine and their fore legs are filled from knees to coronets therefrom. In to-day's mail came a letter from the head of an important Free Library in a nearby city who had been importuned by several customers to put some books on horse training in the library. They applied to me for information and advice, but what was there to tell them? Our trainers who could write a book of real value to the man learning the game cannot be persuaded to do so, or, if they would, cannot put their ideas into the written word. Those trainers who have written their memoirs cannot be said to have added to the available store of written knowledge of the horse industry. We sadly need a companion book on training to Lieutenant-Colonel Wall's books of *Practical Light Horse Breeding* and *Thoroughbred Bloodlines*. All right, come on, who will write it for us?

NOVEMBER 14. This afternoon, on the return trip from the racing at Bowie, I had a look at Granville, which, together with Fore and Riparian, is now at his old home at Belair, in Maryland. Granville I saw galloping in the paddock where I last saw Omaha, a year or so ago. The big bay looks wonderfully well. He's a one man horse, all right, and wants to be "boss" in the stall, as well as on the race track. By now Granville's ankles will have been fired. They're a mite puffy now but apart from that the horse is as sound and fresh as a daisy after his campaign. He's grown in breadth and has filled out into an imposing horse, and he's shorter than one's usual conception of the stayer. Apart from a somewhat sickle hock, which certainly has not hindered his running fast and far, Granville is a grandly made big horse and his action in the paddock as he galloped was superb. Riparian, the stable's Derby hope, though hardly the equal of the past lot, is doing well at Belair as is Fore, a Fairway colt. The Fox's sister, Lucky Pledge, and Valse are there too.

NOVEMBER 15. The cold early breath of winter has reached us today with temperatures just at freezing and a strong wind to make it worse. Had the pleasure of showing our farm to an English Thoroughbred breeding country squire

from the stout old county of Yorkshire this
morning. We spent three hours or so closely
inspecting everything from weanlings to stallions
and our guest's comments were both interesting
and illuminating. The more so as he had just
stopped off for a flying visit after a trip which
included the Blue Grass, Chicago, Toronto, New
York, Bermuda, the Bahamas, Jamaica (where
racing is booming), Cuba, and Miami. I think
that the uniformly good healthy condition of the
horses he saw in American studs impressed our
guest and he commented on the lack of blankets
and the number of racing stock turned out.

NOVEMBER 16. They brought us a big truckload
of corn from the field where the farm crew are
husking this morning, and we will start feeding
it to everything soon now. The infoal mares
here get about half corn and half oats, three
quarts daily of the former and four ears or so
of the latter. The mares in the Madden shed,
ponies, etc., will get more corn than oats. The
weanlings will be getting some of this good
heating food, cracked, along with their crushed
oats and bran. Have been checking over the
mares that were blood-tested for pregnancy this
summer and, as far as we can see now, the test
is just 100 per cent accurate. All of those mares
reported as barren have definitely shown themselves to be so and all of those reported to have
been pregnant now appear to be in foal. One
mare, tested when the hormones were apparently
just showing up at 42 days, and reported as
being very doubtful is certainly barren. Six
mares that have been manually examined for
sale have all shown up in foal, as they were
said to be. All of which influences us favorably
towards this test as a means of early diagnosis
of pregnancy.

NOVEMBER 17. Edgar Horn's voting blank for
the Best Horses poll arrived this morning. We
are supposed to list our three choices in each
of four racing divisions, 2-year-old colts, 2-year-

old fillies, 3-year-olds and best of all ages and sexes. The latter was an easy one to fill, Granville naturally being my pick with Pompoon and Bold Venture in order. Pompoon, too, leads the colts in the juveniles, with Reaping Reward and Maedic next. Apogee, Juliet W., and Wand in 2-year-old fillies and the Belair colt, Bold Venture, and High Fleet among the 3-year-olds completed my scoring. In a couple of weeks we shall see how the consensus of five hundred pickers goes. Something of this sort has been indicated in racing for some time and the enterprising *Turf and Sport Digest* promoted the poll.

NOVEMBER 18. The thermometer has been steadily falling all day and tonight it is down to 23 degrees and still falling. We have baled out all the water troughs and the spigots are cut off so that they will not freeze. Up at the upper farm the men had a cold job building a covered shed in the big stable yard for the newly purchased feeder steers to shelter in. We have half a hundred of these latter and plenty of corn and fodder and other stuff to put in them.

NOVEMBER 19. The thermometer has been down to 15 degrees today. The horses go out and soon get themselves warm, being better off out than in. Things are quieting down into the winter hush of activities which lasts until after the New Year. There is nothing galloping at the training stable. Most of the youngsters are being blistered and finished with saddle work for a couple of months. The weanlings at both places are doing well now and the mares are becoming more sedate. The stallions are all in good order for winter and only one, the lazy scamp, needs more exercise than he will take at liberty in his paddock.

NOVEMBER 20. From the shores of the Great Lakes comes an interesting letter in today's mail, from a gentleman who hunts and breeds in a small way, though with carefully chosen materials. My correspondent sent an apparently healthy mare to a usually very fertile sire last spring, and though every care was taken, no foal resulted. Now the gentleman is interested in finding out whether there is some inoculation which will help his mare. The mare, used for hunting, should, I think, be examined by a veterinarian expert in diagnosing the cause of barrenness, to determine whether there is some ovarian trouble which will prevent her breeding at all. If the vet finds that everything is all right and that cultures prove there is no infection, then it is possible that injections of a wheat-oil germ product, which contains the vitamin responsible for good fertility, vitamin E, might do some good. I am not able to say much of this product, however, as I have never used it.

NOVEMBER 21. Entertained the business manager of a highly successful stud who has a farm not far from us with a number of mares and sires. He reported that bookings to the stallions in his control seem to be coming in a good deal earlier than usual this year, which is a definitely encouraging sign of good conditions in the breeding business.

NOVEMBER 22. A dreary, bleak Sunday. Had a leisurely inspection of the horses this morning and repeated the job this afternoon in company with a young lieutenant of the Army veterinary corps who, ordered to the Philippines, wanted to see as many good horses as he could before banishment. Found the mares off in a protected corner of their field, dodging the cold wind. The weanlings were enjoying a gallop around the paddock, and we tried to pick the stakes winners by their looks and action. Some hope!

NOVEMBER 23. A quiet day, with the men busy cleaning out the stalls after the week-end hiatus in activity. The manure here is now being put into the pen where our lot of steers pack it down well and pick a good bit of roughage from it. The blacksmith went over some few of the

mares' feet and will take care of those at the
Madden shed tomorrow. We have to plan this
week to take in the Thanksgiving holiday.

NOVEMBER 24. The farmers have hauled me a
few loads of fodder which we have stacked near
the corral for feeding during inclement weather.
At the upper farm the farm crew is getting
things in order for a severe winter, which we
are said by the old hands to be in for. At any
rate, we'll have corn a-plenty; over 800 barrels
have gone into the huge new crib already. All
is husked, but more has to come in. The two
young mares that have been at the upper farm
were put out at the shed this afternoon, and
they led the rest a merry chase. They seem
to have settled down tonight and all the mares
are eating at the long trough below the central
hay rack. The stock there are getting plenty of
corn now and are thriving on it.

NOVEMBER 25. We had a representative of a
fertilizer concern here this afternoon. He took
soil samples from six of our fields and paddocks
at the home farm and the firm's agronomists
will report to us in a week or so just how these
fields stand as regards lime and phosphates, as
well as the rest of the minerals. Nowadays firms
and colleges are equipped to diagnose soil
troubles as the laboratories diagnose blood
samples, and one may have prescribed for one's
paddocks the exact "pick-me-up" they require.
It is a far cry from the routine manuring and
liming of my boyhood days, when we went on
the plans our fathers had used for generations.

NOVEMBER 26. Thanksgiving. After a densely
foggy night we got out this morning to the
humming of a brisk cold wind, but a pleasant
sun mitigated things somewhat. All has been
as quiet here today as on an English sabbath.
Had a thorough inspection of everything in my
lot this morning, enjoying the walk around the
paddocks.

NOVEMBER 27. It was sharp, with ice over the water troughs this morning again, and it has become steadily colder all day. I walked through the fields this morning and was struck by the effect of the long fall drought we have experienced here. I do not recall such a long dry spell at this time of the year. The fields are dry all over and as the mares move in the bare spots they kick up dust. There will be little protection for the roots this winter. The blacksmith has been trimming the feet of the weanlings today. They grow fast and on the hard ground break off easily, if left to get too long in the toes. This year they are a straight-footed lot and the smith does not have any special work to do to correct crooked feet, fortunately.

NOVEMBER 28. This morning—a bitterly cold morning it was—the man who feeds at the Madden shed found one of the saddle horses definitely under the weather. She was brought to this end of the farm where we found that she had become chilled during an apparently mild case of colic. The good old stimulant of a toddy was called in, and as it appeared there might be some congestion we gave the patient an injection of neo-salvarsan intravenously. This appeared to straighten her out, and her temperature tonight has dropped from 103 to 101. She is well blanketed and appears much more comfortable just now.

NOVEMBER 29. Somewhat pleasanter today, with a bright sun. Our saddle mount that was sick is much better, and is eating and drinking lightly. Took a long walk to see the stock instead of accompanying the young entry to Sunday School and church, as I suppose I should have done. Everything seems to be going along evenly. Watched the mares and weanlings put up at the upper farm this evening and am pleased with the condition of the former, which are doing well. They consume plenty of soy bean hay now, with good results. The newest arrival among the stallions now has The Major turned out in an adjoining paddock, with only one fence between them, and both enjoy their galloping and playing much more than before.

NOVEMBER 30. Had our first snow flurries this morning, with everything frozen up and the temperature well below normal for this period. Took the new stallion out for a bit of traveling this afternoon. This time he went alongside The Major, leading like an old horse in training and moving freely along without trying to bother me or his partner at all. Today we have put about a score of young pigs in the pound at the upper farm where they will run behind the steers fattening there. These hogs cost little, get no special attention, and grow themselves into cash, while doing their part in improving the soil.

DECEMBER 1. With a heavy snow promised for tonight, the farm crew has hauled a reserve of fodder to my corral where the steers are, and the shelter at that point has been fixed up. Also we have taken care of the water supply, covering well with manure all places where the pipes froze last winter, for we are a month earlier than last year with our freeze. Right by the stable nearest my house there is a yawning hole tonight, for the men have started digging a 14-foot well so that in the future we will not be at the mercy of any more deep wells. The lakes and ponds near here are all frozen over now.

DECEMBER 2. In the early hours of this morning the ground was a couple of inches deep in snow, but it warmed up towards morning with consequent disappearance of the white blanket. Since 10 o'clock it has rained heavily, for which we are thankful. Had the blacksmith check the feet of most of the mares and work stock, as all had to be indoors. One old mule decided that he would have nothing to do with the smith at all, so went into the stocks, soon giving up his

obstreperousness. I blistered one mule this afternoon in the near fore ankle, as he has been
lame there for some time. Also put a blister
on the filling left on the hind leg of the Man o'
War filly that was cut down last summer. This
filly has come on wonderfullly well and will make
a strapping mare before she's through. Received
my Enza-Vita stallion service record book this
morning and suggest that stallion owners send
for one. Pocket size and complete, the book is
a sort of advertising that horsemen will welcome.

DECEMBER 3. Have been filling up the entry
blanks for the Pimlico and Narragansett Futur-
ities today. We have 35 in-foal mares in
each of them. The Maryland affair has an allowance of five pounds for a product of sire and dam
that have produced no winners, three pounds if
only one has produced a winner. The New England outfit has no such allowances. Warmer
weather has followed the rains of yesterday and
all the horses were glad to be out again this
morning, running and kicking up their heels as
they went out. Got the Newmarket final catalogue today, a mere 1,200 entries to scan over,
all to be sold in five days. One notes but one
*Blenheim II mare in the sale, two mares in foal
to this son of Blandford. Only four Blandford
mares are offered. Like the works of a dead
artist, horses improve in value when the parent
stock is gone.

DECEMBER 4. A correspondent from the Buck-
eye State writes in relative to the case of the
foal lost by another correspondent and mentioned
here a couple of weeks ago. The gentleman
stresses that the foal must have all of the dam's
milk for 60 hours, or it will "surely die of impaction of the bowels." This seems a bit strong
to me, for, while the first milk of the dam certainly has cathartic properties, yet many's the
time that I've watched mares run milk for days
and days before foaling, and certainly there was
none of that valuable first milk left. It has never
bothered me, however, for the best regulator of

the mare's milk I ever saw is given through the feed. Since I used the specialty in question I have used but two enemata in some 75 foals born, the mares having the proper regularity of bowel actions and the same applying to their produce.

DECEMBER 5. The veterinarian came and unsexed two of the yearling colts which by their actions had indicated that this sad operation was much needed. Little time was lost about it. A rope was plaited into the tails and passed over the stall wall with a couple of men to hold it tight; another man holds up the near fore leg and yet one more holds the head. In short order the scrotum was washed, the cut made, and the testes drawn out, the cord being emacerated by the instrument used for the purpose. The colts were very quiet and bothered little about the operation. Both were eating hay when I saw them a few minutes ago.

DECEMBER 6. A pouring wet Sunday with everything indoors all day, for this has been a cold driving rain. Examined all the horses in their stalls this morning and found all thriving. One of the youngsters castrated yesterday started to bleed copiously late last night, and it was several hours before treatment was effective in arresting the hemorrhage. He seems to be getting along pretty well tonight, though it is noticeable that he is quite a bit below par. This is a very rare condition and it is the first I have seen at this farm in a large number of castrations.

DECEMBER 7. The weather turned very cold following yesterday's rains, and tonight everything is well frozen over. We have had a couple of the farm men putting a cement floor into two stalls in a barn at the upper farm. These will be used as feed rooms as the dirt floors offer too much attraction for the rats. The cement is poured into a foundation trench two feet deep and four inches wide around the edge of the stall in order that the rats will not burrow and make a harbor under the cement floor. Had a long chat today with an American breeder who has just returned from a visit to England and France. This gentleman reports that the breeding industry is booming and that the large amount of buying being done by representatives of the Russian government has enabled a lot of breeders to dispose of stallions and mares at good prices.

DECEMBER 8. After looking over all the stock this morning I took to the road for our annual mare hunting trip. A couple of other breeders, one newspaperman, and I struck north through Pennsylvania, headed for New Jersey, a more or less new territory, driving in bitterly cold weather.

DECEMBER 9. Still traversing the hinterlands of Pennsylvania and Jersey. Weather cold but not at all unpleasant for driving, and the flat South Jersey terrain looked well and prosperous. Holed up for the night in the famous old horse town of Red Bank. Saw plenty of old friends and talked horse to a fill.

DECEMBER 10. Drove 250 miles homeward today, largely in either pouring rain or fog. Arrived at Sleepy Hollow Stud just in time to get a quick look at most of the horses, finding all in first-class condition. A welcome batch of mail included a press release relative to Dr. Harry H. Laughlin's mathematical method of breeding horses, which he is now reported to have down to fine point. Dr. Laughlin is to speak before a Maryland breeders' group soon.

DECEMBER 11. Spent this morning in a detailed inspection of my lot of horses here, comparing them in the mind's eye with those seen in recent days. It looks as though our stuff is about on an average with most seen, though some of the younger foals are smaller, as is usually the case. The horses were all indoors as the northeaster we drove through yesterday reached here this morning and we had the full benefit of it. The

14-foot wide well that the farm men have been digging in front of the house here has deepened considerably since we went away. The good clay that is coming out of it is going into the bottom of unused stalls and the sheds. Mixed with plenty of lime it becomes just like a cement floor.

DECEMBER 12. The horses have all had an allowance of glauber salts, a good double fistfull apiece, in their water buckets tonight and the grain ration has been cut a third today. This is always done when untoward weather conditions force the horses to remain within doors. Signs that the horse business is steadily forging ahead to good times again are obvious on all sides. Four bids that a few years ago would have meant four buys have so far elicited no cables from Newmarket, so doubtless a wise young California breeder who picked good ones to bid on will be in for a disappointment. Then from the Island possessions comes a cable for information as to the possibilities of obtaining a score of race horses at low cost, not at all an easy order to fill these days, though easily done but a short time past.

DECEMBER 13. This having been a bright and pleasant Sunday, after inspection this morning Mrs. N. V. and I drove over some 50 miles to our State University for lunch with the new head of the Live Stock Department. This gentleman is a keen horseman and our small State is going to be a good deal better off in a few years for his being here. The Federal Government has aided in the building of some new barns at the University and we hope that before long there will be good facilities for students of horse husbandry. The mares and young stock enjoyed their day outside after the continuous cold rains, and all seemed to want to avail themselves of the sand beds for a roll after they had galloped around a bit. Both of the stallions here took a good deal of exercise and before long will be put into regular work.

DECEMBER 14. A windlass has been erected over the well this morning and the strong clay is going into stalls. It seems to take an awful time to get down to water level, and when they do they will have to brick up the sides, so I suppose we will have the mess around for a long time yet. Had a good look at the steers today with the farm manager. They seem to be thriving well and those being fed in the yards at the upper farm are putting on weight nicely. Mine down here are not getting fat but are growing as they should.

DECEMBER 15. The well-diggers have got down some 15 feet and have reached a stratum of pure white sand. We are getting it hauled around the water troughs and gateways, where it becomes very muddy in the winter when it is constantly thawing and freezing. We have also replenished the sand rolling beds in the paddocks, for the mares and young stock seem to enjoy a roll in the cold weather almost as much as they do when it is hot.

DECEMBER 16. I have a letter from the British West Indies today asking me what sort of shoes we use on the feet of our yearlings, and asking whether it is best to shoe them fully or not. Here we put tips, that is half-plates, on them just in front when breaking is started. Usually they are shod with dull-toed plates in front after they have been going along some time and sometimes before they get their final trials shoes are put on behind, though by no means always. We do not use sharp shoes at all on the youngsters, the shoes used being the regular steel racing plates without the toe. I have never seen aluminum plates used on yearling and see little value in them in this case. Some horsemen use no plates at all on yearlings, and, where the feet are in good shape and the footing not too rough, there seems little real need of them. The Thomas Hitchcock horses are regularly left unshod at all times and they certainly win their full share of purses over the jumps.

DECEMBER 17. With Christmas but a week off, we took a day to drive to town and see about seasonal shopping, finding that the garages in the city were packed and stores busy as could be. While awaiting the family I drifted over to the book section of a great store and fell into conversation with a couple of persons who also were intent on scanning the sporting book shelves. Finding that we had similar tastes they asked me if I'd heard about the new book that someone called Salvator was writing about tne year's horses. Having been privileged to peep into this book some weeks ago, I was able to give my opinion that it will be hailed as a great success for its sponsors when it does appear.

DECEMBER 18. Heard from my friends who are in America on a horse-buying mission, and it looks as though their efforts to purchase a score for export will be attended with success. Already they have bought a dozen or so. It will depend on the maritime strike whether they will be able to ship the horses just now, but they are hopeful of getting them out.

DECEMBER 19. It has rained hard all day, with fog as well, but we had a task to do regardless, and from it I have just returned. We drove 50 miles or so this afternoon to look over 45 horses which were sold tonight, at fair prices. Our mission, the acquirement of a teaser, was fulfilled by the purchase of an extremely noisy, though quite nice-looking piebald pony, which, though only a 4-year-old, already has a number of mares in foal to him. He is quite versatile, too. We saw him take several jumps in good style.

DECEMBER 20. A sunny day, with the roads filled all day with people hunting Christmas trees, holly, and what not. Unfortunately most people are not content with picking what they need, but they uselessly destroy a whole tree to get a branch or so. Went over the horses this afternoon and saw all put up for the night. The fields were plenty muddy after yesterday's downpour and most of the stock were well covered with mud. We never bother about this, though, for they will soon roll and get it off and good old mud never hurt a horse's coat yet—though it will bother the heels if they are left uncared for.

DECEMBER 21. We will be busy for the next few days so as to have all in order for the holidays. We will get little done more than caring for the horses in Christmas week. The blacksmith has been going over feet all day, and will do more of them tomorrow. The farm men are seeing that the various barns are well supplied with baled hay, straw, etc., and the steers' wants are being attended to also. The van went up to get our teaser this afternoon and on his arrival here we turned him out in a small paddock which is between one of the stallions and a lot of in-foal mares. The stallion got quite excited and galloped around a good deal, but the mares apparently did not take their new neighbor at all seriously. He's a funny looking piebald and stands only 13 hands, but he has grand action. Tonight he looks a bit lost in a 16x20 loose box. It is big enough for him to exercise in.

DECEMBER 22. Cold and clear, but sunny. Went to the upper farm to see the weanlings go out this morning, and a fine run they took. All are in good shape, and I think the soy bean hay they get is in some measure responsible for their condition, each of them having a good slick coat of hair. I do not recall having a crop of foals do as well at this season in many a year. Placed the new sheets of pedigrees of the newly entered stallions in my *Stallion Register* tonight. The new feature of the list of sires of dams of stakes winners is very useful. The breeder who overlooks entering his sires in this book is missing out on the best and cheapest advertising.

DECEMBER 23. Typed up some lists of the foaling dates of the mares and posted them up in each of the barns this morning. Also put one up in the men's loafing quarters, where it will doubt-less settle a few arguments. Took a drive this afternoon to see that everything was in order around my part of the farm, and then to a friend's farm where some excellent turkeys are raised, one of which he had kindly destined for the Noth-ing Venture Christmas fare. Everything is in pretty good shape now for the holidays and the men are all ready for them, too, though there is not much holidaying around horses.